WORLD PRAISE

Combined Music Edition

Edited by
David Peacock and Geoff Weaver

Jubilate Hymns

Marshall Pickering
An Imprint of HarperCollinsPublishers

Marshall Pickering is an imprint of
HarperCollins*Religious*
Part of HarperCollins*Publishers*
77-85 Fulham Palace Road
Hammersmith, London W6 8JB

This edition first published in Great Britain in 1995 by Marshall Pickering

Compilation copyright © David Peacock and Geoff Weaver

Reprinted
Impression number

The compilers assert the moral right to be identified as the compilers of this work

ISBN 0 551 02956 0

Words edition ISBN 0551 02957 9

Music and text set by Barnes Music Engraving Ltd, East Sussex, England
Printed and bound in Great Britain by

A catalogue record for this book is available from the British Library

For advice on reproducing individual items in this book, see addresses at the back.

Other books edited by the Jubilate Group:

Available from HarperCollins	*Available from Hodder Headline*
Carol Praise	Carols for Today
Hymns for the People	Church Family Worship
Let's Praise!	Hymns for Today's Church
Lollipops	Psalms for Today
World Praise	Songs from the Psalms
Bible Praying	
Prayers for the People	
The Dramatised Bible	

FOREWORD

by the General Secretary of the
Baptist World Alliance

Renewal of worship in the churches is best expressed in the new songs that are being sung. They declare in a contemporary and meaningful way the spiritual desires of our times.

In 1990, the Baptist World Alliance established a Worship Commission as part of the Study and Research Division to seek means of worship appropriate for our generation. The idea for this special commission came out of conversations with Dr. Noel Vose, past president of the BWA, who expressed his concern that there was a crisis of worship in many churches. The commission aims to address the issues and concerns of churches which have lost the joy and spontaneity of Christian worship. David Coffey, General Secretary of the Baptist Union of Great Britain, has been an outstanding chairman. His associate for many years, David Peacock, has also played a key role in the commission. It was his idea that all of us gain a larger vision of the renewal that was happening around the world in many churches. This renewal was being expressed in many ways, but most significantly in the new songs that were being sung.

World Praise is a unique collection of songs from around the world which have brought meaning and dynamism to Christian worship, and an outstanding contribution to the renewal of worship in churches everywhere. Use this book to worship God and praise Christ in a new and living way by the power of the Holy Spirit. Our prayer is that this book of songs will enable a new generation of Christians to join hands, hearts and voices with the world-wide community of believers. May it be said of our generation, 'They sang a new song . . . from every tribe and tongue and people and nation!' (Revelation 5:9).

Denton Lotz
March 1995

PREFACE

World Praise is a unique collection of material drawn from worshipping communities around the world. Here you will find material from every continent – music that crosses denominations and traditions. The items have been chosen because of their ability to travel beyond their place of origin. They range from lively expressions of praise to quiet songs of confession and poignant items yearning for justice.

Texts for most items are in both the original language and in English. In the English translation we have attempted to convey the original meaning as far as possible while trying to fit the text into a regular metrical pattern. We would encourage congregations to sing in the original language wherever appropriate. This combined volume includes a new collection of world worship music together with international hymns and songs which have travelled across the continents and been used in many countries.

The music is arranged with straightforward accompaniments that attempt to capture the authentic nature of each song. Vocal parts, where appropriate, are arranged in four parts. Guitar chords are given for most songs. Each item has performance notes so that congregations are able to sing the different styles of music with integrity.

World Praise can easily be used as a supplement to a congregation's existing repertoire. The book ideally is suited to churches seeking a global perspective within their worship and a broad repertoire for their worship expression. Many items work well alongside hymns and worship-songs. *World Praise* is also useful for missionary services, for international conferences and cross-cultural events, and for congregations made up of a range of nationalities and cultures. The stimulus for this book comes from the Baptist World Alliance's Worship Commission, which is involved in researching different perspectives on worship around the world. The book was used for the first time at the 1995 Baptist World Congress in Argentina.

In recent years, Christians in the West have begun to see mission as more of a partnership – a giving and receiving between different parts of the Body of Christ. Those of us who have so many resources of our own have found it difficult to imagine that we might need to receive from others – or indeed that there might be hidden riches for us to receive. *World Praise* is an opportunity to enrich our worship. In prayer, we can often react intellectually to news of suffering abroad. However, when we sing the songs of Christians in other parts of the world, we are able to enter more fully into their joys and pains. Then we truly understand what Paul means when he writes 'rejoice with those who rejoice and mourn with those who mourn' (Romans 12:15).

David Peacock and Geoff Weaver

LEGAL INFORMATION AND ACKNOWLEDGEMENTS

We are grateful to all those who have provided material for this volume. We thank especially those belonging to Baptist churches around the world and to mission partners of the Church Missionary Society, from whom many of the songs have been collected. We particularly owe our thanks to Michael Perry for his expertise in adapting the texts, and to Laura Werts, Joanna Bennett and Jane Peacock for preparing the material for publication. For the major task of copyright clearance we are deeply grateful to Stanley Grant. We are also grateful for the help of Esther Aeilts, Günter Balders, Dina de Carro, Frank Fortunato, Sue Jones, Inés de Morales and Bruce Muskrat in the translation and collection of material, especially from Latin America.

Every effort has been made to trace copyright owners, and apologies are extended to anyone whose rights have inadvertently not been acknowledged. Any omissions of inaccuracies of copyright details will be corrected in future editions.

Reprinting

Those seeking to reprint material in this book should refer to the addresses given at the back.

SECTION 1:

HYMNS AND SONGS

OF THE

WORLDWIDE CHURCH

1 A BABY WAS BORN IN BETHLEHEM

CARIBBEAN

Words and music: Ivor Golby
arranged Noël Tredinnick

Calypso style ♩ = 114

1 A baby was born in Bethlehem, a baby was born in Bethlehem, a baby was born in Bethlehem — it was Jesus Christ, our Lord.

2 They laid him in a manger, They laid him in a manger, They laid him in a manger — where the ox-en feed on hay.

3 Some shepherds heard the glad tidings, Some shepherds heard the glad tidings, Some shepherds heard the glad tidings — from an angel in the sky.

> The calypso and the Caribbean are almost synonymous.
> Feel the rhythm here rather than counting it mechanically.

4 They left their flocks a-sleeping . . .
  and hurried to Bethlehem.
    Gloria, gloria . . .

5 Three wise men came from far lands . . .
  they were guided by a star.
    Gloria, gloria . . .

6 They laid their gifts before him . . .
  and worshipped on bended knee.
    Gloria, gloria . . .

7 Then everybody be happy . . .
  on the birthday of our Lord!
    Gloria, gloria . . .

2 AHSANTE YESU
We thank you, Jesus

TANZANIA

Words and music: unknown
arranged Geoff Weaver

Simply ♩ = 100

Ah - san - te Ye - su, a - min,   Ah - san - te Ye - su, a -
We thank you, Je - sus; a - men,   we thank you, Je - sus; a -

- min,   Ah - san - te Ye - su, a - min.   Hal - le - lu - jah! A - min.
- men,   we thank you, Je - sus; a - men.   Hal - le - lu - jah! A - men.

Ahsante Yesu, amin,
Ahsante Yesu, amin,
Ahsante Yesu, amin.
Hallelujah! Amin.

We thank you, Jesus; amen,
we thank you, Jesus; amen,
we thank you, Jesus; amen.
Hallelujah! Amen.

A song of thanksgiving, which should be sung with simplicity and gentleness.
One of the gifts of African Christians, often from poor countries like Tanzania, is
their ability to give thanks in all circumstances.

---

3 ALABAD A JEHOVÁ
Praise the Lord

CHILE

Words: from Psalm 107, unknown
Music: Chilean melody
arranged David Peacock

Rhythmically ♩ = 112

A - la - bad a Jeh - o - vá por-que él es bue - no; a - la-
Praise the Lord, let us thank him for his good - ness; praise the

- bad a Jeh - o - vá por-que él es bue - no; a - la-
Lord, let us thank him for his good - ness; praise the

- bad a Jeh - o - vá por-que él es bue - no, por - que pa - ra
Lord, let us thank him for his good - ness, let's praise and a -

siem - pre es su mis - er - i - cor - dia.
- dore him— his mer - cy lasts for ev - er!

An attractive setting of a psalm verse to a popular Chilean melody.
This needs a good rhythmic accompaniment.

4 ALL WHO ARE THIRSTY

PHILIPPINES

Words: from Isaiah 55
Michael Perry
Music: Mutya Lopez Solis
arranged Geoff Weaver

Steadily ♩ = 92

1 All who are thirs - ty,_____ come to the Lord,
2 Why spend your mon - ey,_____ yet have no bread;
3 Call on God's mer - cy_____ while he is near,
4 Where once were bri - ers,_____ flo-wers will grow,

all who are hun - gry,_____ feed on his word;
why work for noth - ing?_____ Trust God in-stead!
turn from your e - vil,_____ come with-out fear;
where lives were bar - ren,_____ riv - ers will flow:

buy with-out pay - ing,_____ food with-out price,
He will pro-vide you_____ rich - est of food:
ask him for par - don =_____ grace will a-bound!
praise to our Sav - iour:_____ grace and re-nown —

Typically Filipino in its blend of joy and melancholy, this song speaks of
the hope that Filipino Christians, so often hit by suffering and oppression,
have in Christ. A guitar accompaniment is very effective here.

eat with thanks-giv - ing_____ God's sac - ri - fice.
come to the wa - ters,_____ drink what is good.
This is the mo - ment_____ he can be found.
ours is the bless - ing,_____ his be the crown!

1 All who are thirsty, come to the Lord,
   all who are hungry, feed on his word;
   buy without paying, food without price,
   eat with thanksgiving God's sacrifice.

2 Why spend your money, yet have no bread;
   why work for nothing? Trust God instead!
   He will provide you richest of food:
   come to the waters, drink what is good.

3 Call on God's mercy while he is near,
   turn from your evil, come without fear;
   ask him for pardon – grace will abound!
   This is the moment he can be found.

4 Where once were briers, flowers will grow,
   where lives were barren, rivers will flow:
   praise to our Saviour: grace and renown –
   ours is the blessing, his be the crown!

5 **ALLELUIA**

SOUTH AFRICA

Words: traditional liturgical text
Music: unknown
transcribed from the singing of George Mxadana

Warmly and purposefully ♩ = 96

Al - le - lu - ia, al - le - lu - ia.

Al - le - lu - ia, al - le - lu - ia. Al -

-le - lu - ia, al - le - lu - ia. Al -

-le - lu - ia, al - le - lu - ia.

South Africans are renowned for the richness of their unaccompanied singing.
This should be sung reflectively rather than boisterously, and should be unaccompanied.

6 ALZA TUS OJOS
Lift up your eyes

Words and music: Juan Salinas
arranged David Peacock

Lively ♩ = 120

Al - za tus o - jos y mi - ra
Lift up your eyes – look a - round you;

la co - se - cha es - tá lis - ta, el
see the fields they are rea - dy, the

tiem - po ha lleg - a - do la
time has come for har - vest. O

mies es - tá ma - du - ra. Es -
Lord, please send more work - ers! Yes,

A popular worship song from Mexico, this item requires a strong rhythmic underlay.

7 AMAHORO BENEDATA
Peace be with you

RWANDA

Words: unknown
Music: unknown
arranged Geoff Weaver

Medium tempo ♩ = 104

LEADER
A - ma - ho - ro be - ne - da - ta
Peace be with you, Christ-ian peo - ple,

ALL
a - ma - ho - ro.
peace be with you.

A - ma - ho - ro kwa Ye - su,
Peace be with you through Je - sus,

a - ma - ho - ro - hal - le - lu - jah!
peace be with you — hal - le - lu - jah!

1	LEADER	*Amahoro benedata*	1	LEADER	Peace be with you, Christian people,	
	ALL	*amahoro.*		ALL	peace be with you.	
		Amahoro kwa Yesu,			Peace be with you through Jesus,	
		amahoro – hallelujah!			peace be with you – hallelujah!	
2	LEADER	*Urekundo, benedata*	2	LEADER	Love be with you, Christian people,	
	ALL	*urekundo . . .*		ALL	love be with you . . .	
3	LEADER	*Munezero, benedata*	3	LEADER	Joy be with you, Christian people,	
	ALL	*munezero . . .*		ALL	joy be with you . . .	

A song suitable for the exchanging of the peace. Like so many African songs, it is unaccompanied and has a leader-response format. The response could be harmonized simply.

8 AMEN, ALLELUIA!

SOUTH AFRICA

Words: traditional
Music: traditional, transcribed from the singing
of George Mxadana and Monica Mothile

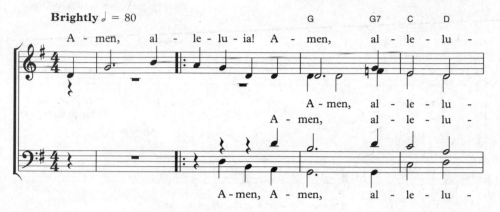

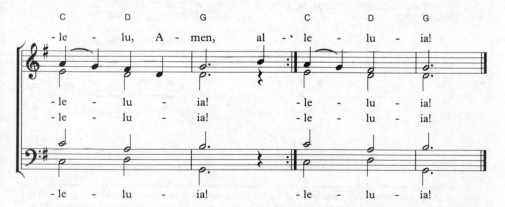

Originally a wedding song, this is a favourite 'going out' song in the worship of the Independent Churches of South Africa. It requires a strong rhythmic sense but should not be sung too quickly.

9 AMEN, SIAKUDUMISA!

Amen, we praise your name, O God

SOUTH AFRICA

Words: unknown
Music: attributed to S. C. Molefe,
as taught by George Mxadana
arranged Dave Dargie

This exuberant song of praise was written by S. C. Molefe at a workshop in South Africa. The harmonies are rich and the 'masithi' from the leader is an encouragement to the congregation. It is very effective in procession, either at the start or at the end of a service.

10 ANTE TU PRESENCIA

Here within your presence

ARGENTINA

Words and music: Daniel di Paolo
English: Word & Music
music arranged David Peacock

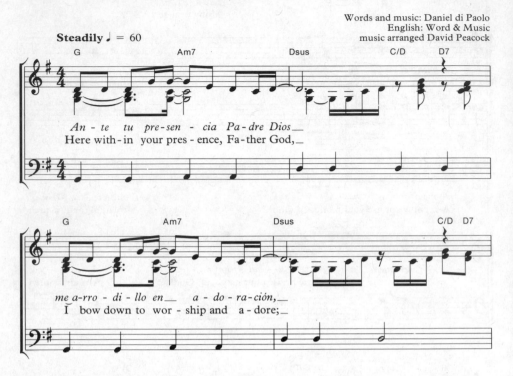

Steadily ♩ = 60

G   Am7   Dsus   C/D   D7

An - te tu pre-sen - cia Pa-dre Dios__
Here with-in your pres - ence, Fa-ther God,__

G   Am7   Dsus   C/D   D7

me a-rro - di - llo en__ a - do - ra - ción,
I bow down to wor - ship and a-dore;__

Em7   Cm   G/B   Em7

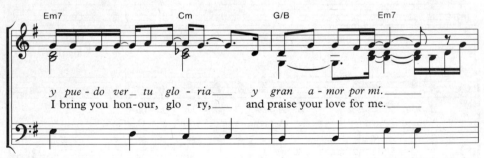

y pue - do ver__ tu glo - ria____ y gran a - mor por mí.____
I bring you hon-our, glo - ry,____ and praise your love for me.____

Am7   G/B   1. Am9/D   D

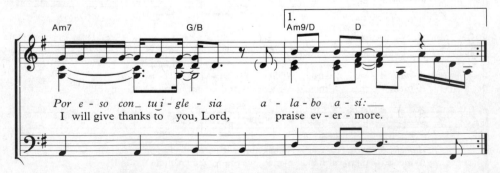

Por e - so con__ tu i - gle - sia a - la - bo a - sí:__
I will give thanks to you, Lord, praise ev - er - more.

> A popular song in Argentina from one of the established
> worship leaders in the country. The song needs to be unhurried.

ti._____   Que tu Es - pí - ri - tu des-cien - da___   y
love;_____   let your Spi - rit, might - y Lord,_____   des -

to - me_es-te lu - gar___   so - la - men - te   pa - ra   tí.
- cend-ing from a - bove,   come and   fill   us   with   your   love.

Ante tu presencia Padre Dios
me arrodillo en adoración,
y puedo ver tu gloria
y gran amor por mí.
Por eso con tu iglesia alabo así:

Ante tu presencia . . .

¡Aleluya! ¡Aleluya!
¡Gloria al Rey de reyes!
¡Gloria al Señor!
¡Aleluya! ¡Aleluya!
Que tu Espíritu descienda
y tome este lugar
solamente para tí.
Que tu Espíritu . . .

Here within your presence, Father God,
I bow down to worship and adore;
I bring you honour, glory, and praise your love for me.
I will give thanks to you, Lord,
praise evermore.

Here within your presence . . .

Alleluia, alleluia,
glory to the Saviour,
praise evermore!
Alleluia, alleluia,
let your Spirit, mighty Lord,
descending from above,
come and fill us with your love;
let your Spirit . . .

11 BANI NGYETI BA YAWE
Let us praise the Lord our God

CAMEROON

Words: unknown
Music: unknown
arranged Geoff Weaver

Ba - ni ngye - ti Ba Ya-we   ba - ni ngye - ti Ba Ya-we
Let us praise the Lord our God,   let us praise the Lord our God,

ba - ni ngye - ti Ba Ya-we.   A - men.   Hal - le - lu-yah,
let us praise the Lord our God.   A - men.   Hal - le - lu-jah,

Hal - le - lu-yah,
Hal - le - lu-jah,

hal - le - lu-yah,   hal - le - lu-yah.   A - men.
hal - le - lu-jah,   hal - le - lu-jah.   A - men.

hal - le - lu-yah,   hal - le - lu - yah.____   A - men.
hal - le - lu-jah,   hal - le - lu - jah.____   A - men.

Bani ngyeti Ba Yawe
bani ngyeti Ba Yawe
bani ngyeti Ba Yawe.
Amen.

Halleluyah, halleluyah,
halleluyah. Amen.

Let us praise the Lord our God,
let us praise the Lord our God,
let us praise the Lord our God.
Amen.

Hallelujah, hallelujah,
hallelujah. Amen.

A joyful West African song which lends itself well to added descants, rhythms and verses and indeed dance. Freedom and exuberance are the watchwords here.

---

12 BIA NENE IFEOMA
How wonderful

NIGERIA

Words and music: unknown
arranged Geoff Weaver

Bia ne - ne___ ifeo - ma Chi - ne - ke Nna
How won - der - ful,___ the things that he has

me - lu mo___ e - ze nkei - gwe e - ke - ne di - li
done for me!___ To God in heaven, to my Lord, glo - ry

o. Bia ne - ne___ ifeo - ma Chi - ne - ke Nna
be. How won - der - ful,___ the things that he has

me - lu mo___ e - ze nkei - gwe e - ke - ne di - li
done for me!___ To God in heaven, to my Lord, glo - ry

This touching song of thanksgiving was sung to the arranger by a Nigerian pastor and his wife, who wanted to give thanks to God in all circumstances. Don't be too worried about meticulous observance of the rhythms.

o. (e - ke - ne di - li o.) Bia ne - ne___ ifeo - ma Chi - ne - ke Nna
be. (to my Lord, glo - ry be.) How won - der - ful,___ the things that he has

me - lu mo___ e - ze nkei - gwe e - ke - ne di - li
done for me!___ To God in heaven, to my Lord, glo - ry

o. Bia ne - ne___ ifeo - ma Chi - ne - ke Nna
be. How won - der - ful,___ the things that he has

me - lu mo___ e - ze nkei - gwe e - ke - ne di - li o.___
done for me! To God in heaven, to my Lord, glo - ry be.___

13 BOLO JAY, MIKAR JAY
Sing my soul, sing to God

INDIA

Words: unknown
Music: unknown
arranged Geoff Weaver

Bo - lo jay,   mi - kar jay,   bo - lo jay   e - shu ki jay;   Bo - lo jay,
Sing my soul,   sing to God,   sing to God, hal - le - lu - jah!   Sing my soul,

bo - lo jay,   bo - lo jay   e - shu ki jay;   bo - lo   jay,   jay,__   jay.
sing to God,   sing to God, hal - le - lu - jah,   hal - le - lu - jah!

Verse

1 Pre - m   ki   te - ri   ye - hi__   reeth__   mu - n ma - y
1 Your love is bound - less,   wide_ as the   o - cean;   fill my heart
2 You_ shed your pre - cious blood to give re - demp - tion;   now that I am

> This gentle and simple song of praise was sung to the arranger by an Indian pastor's wife. The verse could very effectively be sung as a solo, the chorus by all.

bha - r dey a - pa - ni___ preeth. Te - rey pre - m ke ga - ye___
with your love, may I love you more. Let me dai - ly___ sing_ of your
free from guilt, may I love you more.

geeth, te - rey pre - m ke ga - ye___ geeth.
love, let me dai - ly___ sing_ of your love.

Bolo jay, mikar jay,
bolo jay eshu ki jay;
Bolo jay, bolo jay,
bolo jay eshu ki jay;
bolo jay, jay, jay.

1 Prem ki teri yehi reeth
mun may bhar dey apani preeth.
Prem ki teri . . .
Terey prem ke gaye geeth,
terey prem ke gaye geeth.
Bolo jay . . .

Sing my soul, sing to God,
sing to God, hallelujah!
Sing my soul, sing to God,
sing to God, hallelujah, hallelujah!

1 Your love is boundless, wide as the ocean;
fill my heart with your love, may I love you more.
Your love . . .
Let me daily sing of your love,
let me daily sing of your love.
Sing my soul . . .

2 You shed your precious blood to give redemption;
now that I am free from guilt, may I love you more.
You shed . . .
Let me daily sing of your love,
let me daily sing of your love.
Sing my soul . . .

14 BY THE BABYLONIAN RIVERS

LATVIA

Words: from Psalm 137
Ewald Bash
Music: Latvian melody
arranged Geoff Weaver

1 By the Babylonian rivers we sat down in grief and wept; hung our harps upon a willow, mourned for Zion while we slept.

2 There our captors, in derision, did require of us a song; so we sat with staring vision and the days were hard and long.

3 How shall we sing the Lord's song in a strange and bitter land; can our voices veil the sorrow? Lord God, hear your lonely band.

4 Let your cross be benediction for all bound in tyranny; by the power of resurrection loose them from captivity.

This melancholy Latvian folk melody reflects beautifully the desolation of the exiles. This is very effective when sung unaccompanied or with simple guitar accompaniment.

15 BY THE WATERS OF BABYLON

ISRAEL

Words: from Psalm 137
Music: Israeli folk melody
arranged Geoff Weaver

By_____ the wa – ters, the wa – ters of Ba – by-lon,

we sat down and wept, and wept_ for you, Zi - on;

we re-mem-ber, we re-mem-ber, we re-mem-ber you, Zi - on.

The source of this very effective canon is uncertain. As with all canons, ensure that it is well known before dividing the congregation.

16 CANTAI AO SENHOR
O sing to the Lord

BRAZIL

Words: anonymous
translated Gerhard Cartford
Music: Brazilian folksong
arranged Christopher Norton

A lively Brazilian worship song that can be enhanced by a range of percussive sounds and joyful dancing.

Music arrangement: © 1993 Christopher Norton / HarperCollins*Religious* /
CopyCare Ltd., P. O. Box 77, Hailsham,
East Sussex BN27 3EF, UK. Used by permission.

Words: Portuguese Copyright control
English translation © Gerhard Cartford

1 Cantai ao Senhor um cântico novo,
cantai ao Senhor um cântico novo,
cantai ao Senhor um cântico novo,
cantai ao Senhor, cantai ao Senhor!

2 Porque ele fez, ele faz maravilhas,
porque ele fez, ele faz maravilhas,
porque ele fez, ele faz maravilhas,
cantai ao Senhor, cantai ao Senhor!

3 Cantai ao Senhor, bendizei o seu nome,
cantai ao Senhor, bendizei o seu nome,
cantai ao Senhor, bendizei o seu nome,
cantai ao Senhor, cantai ao Senhor!

4 É ele quem dá o Espíritu Santo,
é ele quem dá o Espíritu Santo,
é ele quem dá o Espíritu Santo,
cantai ao Senhor, cantai ao Senhor!

5 Jesus é o Senhor! Amén, aleluia!
Jesus é o Senhor! Amén, aleluia!
Jesus é o Senhor! Amén, aleluia!
cantai ao Senhor, cantai ao Senhor!

1 O sing to the Lord, O sing God a new song,
O sing to the Lord, O sing God a new song;
O sing to the Lord, O sing God a new song –
O sing to our God, O sing to our God!

2 For God is the Lord and God has done wonders,
for God is the Lord and God has done wonders;
for God is the Lord and God has done wonders –
O sing to our God, O sing to our God!

3 So dance for our God and blow all the trumpets,
so dance for our God and blow all the trumpets;
so dance for our God and blow all the trumpets –
O sing to our God, O sing to our God!

4 O shout to our God, who gave us the Spirit,
O shout to our God, who gave us the Spirit;
O shout to our God, who gave us the Spirit –
O sing to our God, O sing to our God!

5 For Jesus is Lord, Amen! Alleluia!
For Jesus is Lord, Amen! Alleluia!
For Jesus is Lord, Amen! Alleluia!
O sing to our God, O sing to our God!

17 CAST YOUR BURDENS (HIYA, HIYA)

Higher, higher

EAST AFRICA

Words and music: Issac Balinda
arranged Geoff Weaver

Rhythmically ♩ = 112

African Christians worship in dance as readily as in song, and this rhythmic song, very popular in East Africa, almost demands some simple actions.

1 Cast your burdens on to Jesus,
   for he cares for you;
   cast your burdens on to Jesus,
   for he cares for you.
       Higher, higher,
       higher, higher, higher,
       higher, higher, higher,
       lift Jesus higher!
       Higher, higher,
       higher, higher, higher,
       higher, higher, higher,
       lift Jesus higher!

2 When you're weary, follow Jesus:
   for he cares for you;
   when you're weary, follow Jesus:
   for he cares for you.
       Follow, follow,
       follow, follow, follow,
       follow, follow, follow,
       follow Jesus, follow!
       Follow, follow,
       follow, follow, follow,
       follow, follow, follow,
       follow Jesus, follow!

       Higher, higher . . .

18 CHRIST IS ALL TO ME

INDIA

Words: after Y. Gnanamani
D. T. Niles
Music: Tamil melody
arranged Geoff Weaver

Expressively ♩ = 104

Chorus

Christ is all to me, Je-sus Christ is all to me;
in this world of strife and sor-row, Christ is all to me.

Verse

1 Christ a bro-ther is to me
2 Watch-ing me with shep-herd-care,
3 Peace when storms a-round me blow,
4 Teach-er of the truth of God,
5 He the prize and he the goal,

The great Sri Lankan Christian leader, D. T. Niles, based this hymn of commitment and trust in Christ upon a Tamil text, and appropriately set it to a Tamil melody.

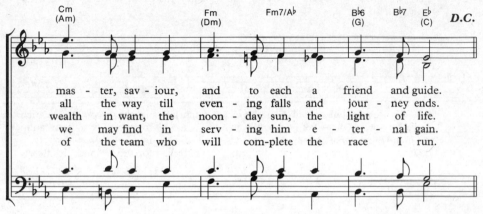

Christ is all to me,
Jesus Christ is all to me;
in this world of strife and sorrow,
Christ is all to me.

1   Christ a brother is to me –
bridegroom he, the Church his bride;
parent, teacher, master, saviour,
and to each a friend and guide.
Christ is all to me . . .

2 Watching me with shepherd-care,
lovingly my needs attends,
my companion all the way
till evening falls and journey ends.
  Christ is all to me . . .

3 Peace when storms around me blow,
joy in sorrow, calm in strife;
health in sickness, wealth in want,
the noonday sun, the light of life.
  Christ is all to me . . .

4 Teacher of the truth of God,
prophet of God's heavenly reign;
sent by God that we may find
in serving him eternal gain.
  Christ is all to me . . .

5 He the prize and he the goal,
and by him the race begun;
he the runner of the team
who will complete the race I run.
  Christ is all to me . . .

19 CHRIST'S IS THE WORLD IN WHICH WE MOVE

SCOTLAND

A TOUCHING PLACE

Words: John L. Bell
and Graham Maule
Music: 'Dream Angus'
arranged John L. Bell
and Graham Maule

♩ = 138 (♩. = 46)

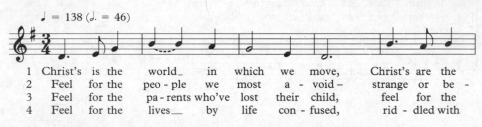

1 Christ's is the world_ in which we move, Christ's are the
2 Feel for the peo-ple we most a-void_ strange or be-
3 Feel for the pa-rents who've lost their child, feel for the
4 Feel for the lives_ by life con-fused, rid-dled with

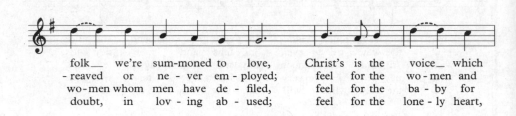

folk_ we're sum-moned to love, Christ's is the voice_ which
-reaved or ne-ver em-ployed; feel for the wo-men and
wo-men whom men have de-filed, feel for the ba-by for
doubt, in lov-ing ab-used; feel for the lone-ly heart,

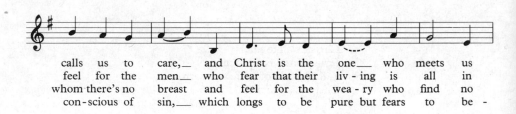

calls us to care,_ and Christ is the one_ who meets us
feel for the men_ who fear that their liv-ing is all in
whom there's no breast and feel for the wea-ry who find no
con-scious of sin,_ which longs to be pure but fears to be-

here.
vain.   To the lost Christ shows his face;
rest.
-gin.

'A Touching Place' from the *Love from Below* collection

This song is frequently used at healing services as people come forward
to have hands laid on them. Then, or at other times, it is best suited to
one solo voice singing the verses and all joining in the chorus.

to the un - loved he gives his em - brace;___
to those who cry___ in pain or dis - grace___ Christ
makes, with his friends, a touch - ing place.___

1 Christ's is the world in which we move,
   Christ's are the folk we're summoned to love,
   Christ's is the voice which calls us to care,
   and Christ is the one who meets us here.
      To the lost Christ shows his face;
      to the unloved he gives his embrace;
      to those who cry in pain or disgrace
      Christ makes, with his friends, a touching place.

2 Feel for the people we most avoid –
   strange or bereaved or never employed;
   feel for the women and feel for the men
   who fear that their living is all in vain.
      To the lost . . .

3 Feel for the parents who've lost their child,
   feel for the women whom men have defiled,
   feel for the baby for whom there's no breast
   and feel for the weary who find no rest.
      To the lost . . .

4 Feel for the lives by life confused,
   riddled with doubt, in loving abused;
   feel for the lonely heart, conscious of sin,
   which longs to be pure but fears to begin.
      To the lost . . .

20 CLEAR AND CALM THE NIGHT

CHINA

Words: Zhi Wei and Wu Jing-reu
English: Brynmor Price and Michael Ball
Music: Shi Qu-gui

1 Clear and calm the night – ho - ly night of
2 Clear and calm the night – ho - ly night of
3 Clear and calm the night – ho - ly night of

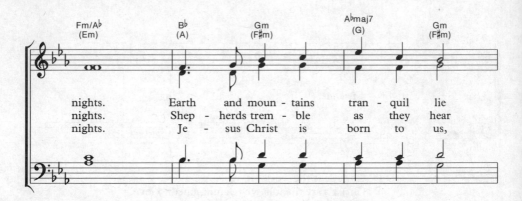

nights. Earth and moun - tains tran - quil lie
nights. Shep - herds trem - ble as they hear
nights. Je - sus Christ is born to us,

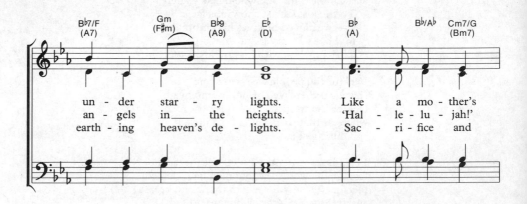

un - der star - ry lights. Like a mo - ther's
an - gels in the heights. 'Hal - le - lu - jah!'
earth - ing heaven's de - lights. Sac - ri - fice and

> This tranquil Christmas song was one of more than fifty composed for the new Chinese Hymnal, published in 1983 to serve the post-denominational Church in China. Its restful character reflects the hope of a more peaceful future after the turbulence of the Cultural Revolution. It may be sung as a solo or by full choir.

1   Clear and calm the night –
holy night of nights.
Earth and mountains tranquil lie
under starry lights.
Like a mother's arms, the hills
embrace the holy town of Bethlehem
where the heavenly Babe lies in stable bare.

2   Clear and calm the night –
holy night of nights.
Shepherds tremble as they hear
angels in the heights.
'Hallelujah!' echoes back from earth;
news with jade harps sounded out –
good news for us all of the Saviour's birth.

3   Clear and calm the night –
holy night of nights.
Jesus Christ is born to us,
earthing heaven's delights.
Sacrifice and joy and peace and love,
righteousness, forgiveness, hope
shine from Jesus' face – glory from above!

21 COME NOW WITH JOYFUL AND THANKFUL HEARTS

INDIA

Words: from Psalm 95
James Minchin
Music: Karnatic hymn melody
arranged I-to-Loh

1 Come now with joyful and thankful hearts,
2 Know that the Lord is our mighty God,
3 He has created the deep blue sea,

into the courts of the King of kings;
ruler supreme in the realms above;
his own hands made the beautiful land;

come now with joyful and thankful hearts,
know that the Lord is our mighty God,
he has created the deep blue sea,

into the courts of the King of kings.
ruler supreme in the realms above.
his own hands made the beautiful land.

The Karnatic repertoire, from India, is a rich and living resource. Over a drone and repeated rhythm (perhaps played on the tambour) the melody should be strongly rhythmic.

Come and re-joice in his won-drous works —
He is the Lord of the depths be-low,
Gen - tle and kind, the Good Shep - herd he –

thank him and praise___ him with joy - ful___ psalms.___
he is the strength___ of the moun - tains_ high.___
we are the sheep___ of his pas - ture - land.___

Come_ now with joy - ful and thank - ful hearts

in - to the courts of the King of___ kings.

4 Come, let us bow down and worship him,
    kneel in the presence of our great God;
    come, let us bow down and worship him,
    kneel in the presence of our great God.
    If you will listen and heed his word,
    you shall be glad and your heart rejoice.
        Come now with . . .

5 Glory to Father and glory to Son,
    glory to Spirit and Three-in-One;
    glory to Father and glory to Son,
    glory to Spirit and Three-in-One.
    Glory to God when the worlds began,
    glory to him evermore shall be!
        Come now with . . .

22 CHU YŎ SA SŬ MI SHI NAEN MUL

My soul longs for you

KOREA

Words: from Psalm 42
Music: Geonyong Lee

Expressively ♩ = 108

PART 1

Chu yŏ___ sa sŭ mi___ shi naen mul___
My soul___ longs for you,___ O my God,___

PART 2

Chu yŏ___ sa sŭ mi___ shi naen mul___
My soul___ longs for you,___ O my God,

ch'at tŭt___ nae nŏk si chu rŭl ch'at sŭm ni da.___
as a deer___ longs for flow - ing streams, for flow-ing streams.___

___ ch'at tŭt___ nae nŏk si chu rŭl ch'at sŭm ni
___ my God,___ longs for flow - ing streams, thirsts for my

___ Kal kŭ p'an nae yŏng hon i sa ra ge shin
___ My soul thirsts for God, for God, the liv - ing God:

da. Kal kŭ p'an nae yŏng hon i sa ra ge
God, for my God, the liv - ing God: when shall I

chu___ ni mŭl ŏn che na poe o ri kka.
when shall I come to be - hold_ the face of my God?

shin chu ni mŭl ŏn che na poe o ri. kka.___
come, shall I come, to be - hold_ the face of my God?

This haunting two-part setting of words from Psalm 42 is best sung unaccompanied, following the natural accents of the text. Geonyong Lee has waited and
yearned for justice and re-unification in his country of Korea, and this song
powerfully reflects that longing.

23 COME NOW, O PRINCE OF PEACE

Words: Geonyong Lee;
paraphrased by Marion Pope; altered
Music: Geonyong Lee

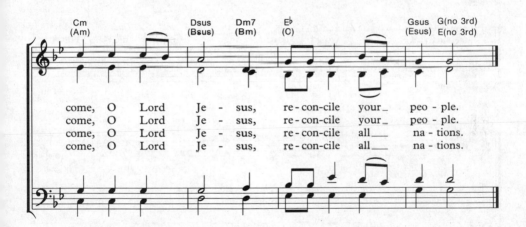

1 Come now, O Prince of peace,
make us one body,
come, O Lord Jesus,
reconcile your people.

2 Come now, O God of love,
make us one body,
come, O Lord Jesus,
reconcile your people.

3 Come now and set us free,
O God, our Saviour,
come, O Lord Jesus,
reconcile all nations.

4 Come, Hope of unity,
make us one body,
come, O Lord Jesus,
reconcile all nations.

For most Korean Christians reunification of North and South Korea is their priority, and their urgent prayer. Geonyong Lee, one of the leading contemporary composers in Korea, has long identified himself with this struggle. Note how the dissonant harmonies paint the discord within the nation. This is very effective when sung unaccompanied.

24 CORDERO NG DIYOS
O Lamb of God

PHILIPPINES

AGNUS DEI

Words: traditional
Music: unknown
arranged David Peacock

Expressively with rhythm ♩ = 100

Cor - de - ro ng Diyos na na - ga - a - lis, ng mg-
O Lamb of God you take a - way the

-a ka - sa - la - nan ng san - li - bu - tan. Ma -
sins of the world, have mer - cy on us. Have

-a - wa ka, ma - a - wa ka, sa a -
mer - cy, have mer - cy, have mer -

- cy, min. Cor - de - ro ng
Lord. O Lamb of

> A beautiful song from the Philippines, where the long history
> of suffering makes this prayer for mercy so poignant.

Diyos na na - ga - a - lis, ng mg - a ka - sa - la-nan ng
God you_ take a - way the_ sins of the world, have

san - li - bu - tan. I - pag - ka - loob_____ mo ang
mer-cy on us. Have mer - cy,_ have mer -

i - yong ka - pa - ya - pa - an._____
- cy, and____ grant, O grant us peace._____

Cordero ng Diyos na nagaalis,
ng mga kasalanan ng sanlibutan.
Maawa ka, maawa ka, sa amin.

O Lamb of God you take away
the sins of the world, have mercy on us.
Have mercy, have mercy,
have mercy, Lord.

Cordero ng Diyos na nagaalis,
ng mga kasalanan ng sanlibutan.
Ipagkaloob mo ang iyong kapayapaan.

O Lamb of God you take away
the sins of the world, have mercy on us.
Have mercy, have mercy,
and grant, O grant us peace.

25 CRISTO VIVE
Christ is risen

ARGENTINA

Words: after Nicolas Martinez
Fred Kaan
Music: Pablo D. Sosa

Confidently ♩ = 116

1 ¡Cris-to vi - ve, fue-ra el llan - to, los la-men - tos y el pe-
2 Que si Cris - to no vi - vie - ra va-na fue - ra nues-tra-
1 Christ is ris - en, Christ is liv - ing, dry your tears, be un - a-
2 If the Lord had ne - ver ris - en, we'd have noth - ing to be-

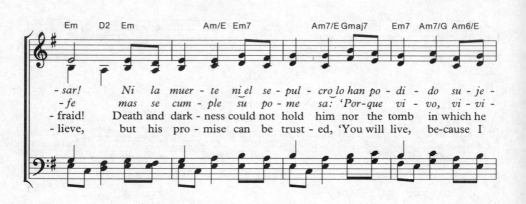

- sar! Ni la muer - te ni el se-pul - cro lo han po - di - do su-je-
- fe mas se cum - ple su po-me - sa: 'Por-que vi - vo, vi-vi-
- fraid! Death and dark - ness could not hold him nor the tomb in which he
- lieve, but his pro - mise can be trust - ed, 'You will live, be-cause I

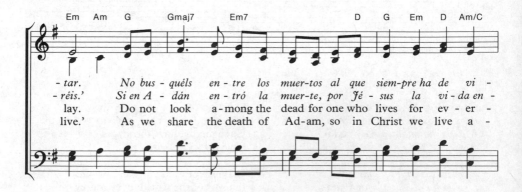

- tar. No bus - qués en - tre los muer-tos al que siem-pre ha de vi-
- réis.' Si en A - dán en - tró la muer-te, por Jé - sus la vi-da en-
lay. Do not look a-mong the dead for one who lives for ev - er-
live.' As we share the death of Ad-am, so in Christ we live a-

> Coming out of a situation of oppression and anguish, reflected in the minor
> key, this Easter song brings hope; the spirit of the dance is never far away.

1. ¡Cristo vive, fuera el llanto, los lamentos y el pesar!
   Ni la muerte ni el sepulcro lo han podido sujetar.
   No busquéls entre los muertos al que siempre ha de vivir
   ¡Cristo vive! estats nuevas por doquier dejad oir.

2. Que si Cristo no viviera vana fuera nuestrafe
   mas se cumple su pome sa: 'Porque vivo, viviréis.'
   Si en Adán entró la muerte, por Jésus la vida entró
   no temáis, el triunfo es vuestro ¡El Señor resucitó!

3. Si es verdad que de la muerte el pecado es aguijón
   no temáis pues Jesucristo nos da vida y salvacion.
   Gracias demos al Dios Padre que nos da seguridad
   que quien cree en Jesucristo vive por la eternidad.

1. Christ is risen, Christ is living,
        dry your tears, be unafraid!
   Death and darkness could not hold him
        nor the tomb in which he lay.
   Do not look among the dead
        for one who lives for evermore;
   tell the world that Christ is risen,
        make it known he goes before.

2. If the Lord had never risen,
        we'd have nothing to believe,
   but his promise can be trusted,
        'You will live, because I live.'
   As we share the death of Adam,
        so in Christ we live again;
   death has lost its sting and terror,
        Christ the Lord has come to reign.

3. Death has lost its old dominion:
        let the world rejoice and shout!
   Christ the firstborn of the living,
        gives us life and leads us out.
   Let us thank our God who causes
        hope to spring up from the ground.
   Christ is risen! Christ is giving
        life eternal, life profound.

26 DANOS UN CORAZÓN GRANDE PARA AMAR

God, give us a new heart

EL SALVADOR

Words: from the Salvadorian
in this version Word & Music
Music arranged Christopher Norton

So great has been the suffering of the people of El Salvador that the prayer for a new heart, a heart which can love rather than hate, must be a very powerful one. There is strength and determination about this song, and the rhythms of the dance are never far below the surface.

-ten - cia co - mo___ ries-go de un lar - go ca - mi - nar.
-ven - ture as___ they_ go on their long__ pil-grim-age:
chains – free-dom-lov-ing peo-ple, de-mand-ing li - ber - ty:
poor – shar-ing with_ them_ their homes and their bread.

Danos un corazón grande para amar.
Danos un corazón fuerte para luchar.

1 *Gentes nuevos, creadores de la historia*
constructores de nueva humanidad.
Gentes nuevos que viven la existencia
como riesgo de un largo caminar.
        Danos . . .

2 *Gentes nuevos luhando en esperanza*
caminantessedientes de verdad
gentes nuevos sin frenos ni cadenas
gentes libres que exigen libertad.
        Danos . . .

3 *Gentes nuevos amando sin fronteras*
por encima de razas y lugar
gentes nuevos al lado de los pobres
compartiendo con ellos techo y pan.
        Danos . . .

God, give us a new heart,
big enough to love;
God, give us a new heart,
strong enough to fight.

1 Renewed people, creators of history –
builders of a new humanity;
renewed people who live with adventure
as they go on their long pilgrimage:
        God, give us . . .

2 Renewed people, struggling in hope –
thirsty pilgrims, seeking truth and light;
renewed people, now free from all their chains –
freedom-loving people, demanding liberty:
        God, give us . . .

3 Renewed people, loving without limit –
without regard to race or pride of place;
renewed people, standing by the poor –
sharing with them their homes and their bread.
        God, give us . . .

27 DÄR GUDS ANDE ÄR
Where the Spirit is

SWEDEN

Words and music: Jonas Jonson
arranged Geoff Weaver

A joyful song of freedom in the Spirit from one of Sweden's most prolific contemporary hymn writers. This needs to move, one in a bar, with great rhythmic drive.

28 DIOS ES NUESTRO AMPARO
Jesus is our refuge

Words: from Psalm 46 and Revelation 1
paraphrased Michael Perry
Music: Chilean melody
arranged David Peacock

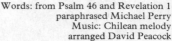

Lively ♩ = 120

1 *Dios es nues-tro am-paro,* *nues-tra for-ta-le-za,*
2 *Hay un río lim-pio de* *a-guas cris-ta-li-nas*
1 Je-sus is our re-fuge, he is with us al-ways,
2 See the might-y ri-ver flow-ing from God's ci-ty,

nues-tro pron-to aux-ilio en la tri-bu-la-ción,
en la ciu-dad san-ta, mor-ada de Je-ho-vá.
com-ing to our res-cue, and so we will not fear.
bless-ings from the glo-ry, the place where Je-sus reigns!

Aun-que se tras-pas-en los mon-tes a la mar y aun-
Dios es-tá en el-la y fir-me es-ta-rá,_____ al
Though the moun-tains trem-ble, and though the earth is sha-king, our
Na-tions are in up-roar, the peo-ple faint with ter-ror, but

A popular melody in Latin America that has been set to Psalm 46.
It may be helpful to include an instrumental verse.

- que la tier - ra tiem — ble te — ne - mos que con - fiar.
clar - ear la ma - ña — na su ay - u - da tra - erá.
Sav - iour will re - deem us, our Lord is com - ing near.
Je - sus Christ is com — ing and he will break our chains.

1 Dios es nuestro amparo, nuestra fortaleza,
   nuestro pronto auxilio en la tribulación,
   Aunque se traspasen los montes a la mar y aunque
   la tierra tiemble tenemos que confiar.
   Aunque se traspasen . . .

2 Hay un río limpio de aguas cristalinas
   en la ciudad santa, morada de Jehová.
   Dios está en ella y firme estará,
   al clarear la mañana su ayuda traerá.
   Dios está en ella . . .

3 Bramaron las naciones, reinos titubearon.
   El dio la palabra: la tierra derritió.
   Con nosotros siempre Jehová está,
   el es nuestro refugio, tenemos que confiar.
   Con nosotros siempre . . .

1 Jesus is our refuge,
      he is with us always,
   coming to our rescue,
      and so we will not fear.
   Though the mountains tremble,
      and though the earth is shaking,
   our Saviour will redeem us,
      our Lord is coming near.
   Though the mountains . . .

2 See the mighty river
      flowing from God's city,
   blessings from the glory,
      the place where Jesus reigns!
   Nations are in uproar,
      the people faint with terror,
   but Jesus Christ is coming
      and he will break our chains.
   Nations are in uproar . . .

3 Come and see the wonders
      he will do from heaven,
   ending all aggression
      and bringing peace to birth.
   Everyone will see him
      and bow before their master;
   for he will be exalted
      and praised through all the earth.
   Everyone will see him . . .

29 DU ÄR HELIG
You are holy

SWEDEN

Words and music: Per Harling
arranged David Peacock

Du är he - lig, du är hel.___ Du är all - tid my-cket mer,___
You are ho - ly, you are whole; you are al - ways so much more

___ än vi na - nsin kan för - sta,___ du är
___ than we ev - er un - der - stand. ___ You are

nä - ra än - da.___ Väl - sig - nad___ va - re du___
al - ways at hand. ___ Bless - èd are you com-ing near,

An interesting cultural mix, with a modern Swedish song writer making use of the samba rhythm. It is very effective to divide the congregation into two and to sing this as a round (the second group starts when the first group has reached Part 2). A strong rhythmic drive is essential throughout.

-lu - ja,___   hal - le - lu - ja,___
-lu - jah,___   hal - le - lu - jah,___

hal - le - lu - ja,___ var Gud.
hal - le - lu - jah,___ our Lord!

Du är helig, du är hel.
Du är alltid mycket mer,
    än vi nansin kan första,
du är nära ända.
Välsignad vare du
som kommer hit just nu,
välsgnande var jord,
    blir till bröd pa var jord.
Du är helig, du är helhet, du är närhet,
hela kosmos lovar Dig!
Halleluja, halleluja, halleluja, halleluja, var Gud.

You are holy, you are whole;
you are always so much more
    than we ever understand.
You are always at hand.
Blessèd are you coming near,
blessèd are you coming here
    to your church in wine and bread,
raised from soil, raised from dead.
You are holy, you are wholeness,
you are present:
let the cosmos praise you, Lord.
Hallelujah, hallelujah, hallelujah, hallelujah, our Lord!

30 EWURADZE
Lord, have mercy

GHANA

KYRIE

Music: unknown
arranged Geoff Weaver

Prayerfully ♩ = 100

1 & 3 E - wu-ra - dze hun yen mbo-bor, E - wu-ra -
2 Christ_____ hun yen mbo-bor, Christ_____
1 & 3 Lord,_____ have mer - cy, Lord,_____
2 Christ,_____ have mer - cy, Christ,_____

- dze hun yen mbo-bor. Ao Ewu-ra - dze,_____ Ao Ewu-ra -
__ hun yen mbo-bor. A - wa-nwa Christ,_____ a - wa-nwa_
__ have mer - cy. Have mer-cy, Lord, have mer-cy, O__
__ have mer - cy. Have mer-cy, Christ, have mer-cy, O__

- dze, E - wu-ra - dze hun yen_____ mbo - bor.
Christ. Christ_____ hun yen_____ mbo - bor.
Lord, Lord,_____ have mer - cy.
Christ. Christ,_____ have mer - cy.

> A beautiful song from Ghana, originally in the
> Fante language. It should be sung *a cappella*.

31 EL CIELO CANTA ALEGRÍA
Heaven is singing for joy

ARGENTINA

Words and music: Pablo D. Sosa
arranged Geoff Weaver

With joy and movement ♩ = 112

1 El cie-lo can-ta a-le-grí-a, ¡A-le-lu - ya!
2 El cie-lo can-ta a-le-grí-a, ¡A-le-lu - ya!
1 Hea-ven is sing-ing for joy.__ Al-le-lu - ia!
2 Hea-ven is sing-ing for joy.__ Al-le-lu - ia!

por-que en tu vi-da y la mí-a bri-lla la glo - ria de Dios.
por-que a tu vi-da y la mí-a las une el a - mor de Dios.
For in your life and__ mine is shin-ing the glo - ry of God.
For your__ life and__ mine are one in the love of__ God.

¡A - le - lu - ya, a - le - lu - ya,
Al - le - lu - ia, al - le - lu - ia,

Pablo Sosa is one of the most prolific of Argentinian hymn and songwriters, and this joyful dance song should be sung with rhythm and with abandon! A percussion accompaniment helps to highlight its dance-like character.

a - le - lu - ya, a - le - lu - ya!
al - le - lu - ia, al - le - lu - ia!

1   El cielo canta alegría, ¡Aleluya!
    porque en tu vida y la mía brilla la gloria de Dios.
    ¡Aleluya, aleluya, aleluya, aleluya!

2   El cielo canta alegría, ¡Aleluya!
    porque a tu vida y la mía las une el amor de Dios.
    ¡Aleluya, aleluya, aleluya, aleluya!

3   El cielo canta alegría, ¡Aleluya!
    porque a tu vida y la mía proclamarán al Señor.
    ¡Aleluya, aleluya, aleluya, aleluya!

1   Heaven is singing for joy. Alleluia!
    For in your life and mine is shining the glory of God.
    Alleluia, alleluia, alleluia, alleluia!

2   Heaven is singing for joy. Alleluia!
    For your life and mine are one in the love of God.
    Alleluia, alleluia, alleluia, alleluia!

3   Heaven is singing for joy. Alleluia!
    For your life and mine will always proclaim the Lord.
    Alleluia, alleluia, alleluia, alleluia!

32 EL SEÑOR ÉS LA MEVA FORÇA
In the Lord I'll be ever thankful

FRANCE

Words: Taizé
Music: Jacques Berthier

♩ = 69

Capo 3(D) Dm C   F   B♭ C   Dm C   F
        (Bm) (A) (D)   (G) (A) (Bm)(A) (D)

El Se - ñor és la me - va for - ça, el Se - ñor el me - u
In the   Lord I'll be ev - er thank - ful, in the Lord I will re -

C   B♭   A   Dm   C
(A)   (G)   (F♯)   (Bm)   (A)

cant.   Ell m'ha e - stat   la sal - va - ci - ó.   En ell con -
- joice. Trust in God,   do not be a - fraid.   Our hearts un -

F   B♭   C   Am   Dm   B♭ C   F
(D)   (G)   (A)   (F♯m) (Bm)   (G) (A) (D)

- fi - o, i no tinc por. En ell con - fi - o, i no tinc por.
- trou - bled, the Lord is near, our hearts un - trou - bled, the Lord is near.

Words and music: © Ateliers et Presses de Taizé

El Señor és la meva força,
el Señor el meu cant.
Ell m'ha estat
la salvació.
En ell confío,
i no tinc por.
En ell confío,
i no tinc por.

In the Lord I'll be ever thankful,
in the Lord I will rejoice.
Trust in God,
do not be afraid.
Our hearts untroubled,
the Lord is near,
our hearts untroubled,
the Lord is near.

33 EN TI CONFIA MI CORAZÓN
O Lord, you are my confidence

MEXICO

From Psalm 62
Words and music: Lorena Warren
in this version Word & Music
arranged David Peacock

With expression ♩ = 80

En ti con-fí-a_____ mi
O Lord, you are_____ my

co-ra-zón,_____ en ti re-po-sa_____ mi
con-fi-dence, in you I am_____ con-

al-ma. Mi ser desc-an-sa_____ en
-tent-ed; O Lord, my re-fuge_____ and

ti pue-do ser_____ fe-liz._____ En
rock, I find rest_____ in you._____ O

A good number of Mexican worship songs are sung throughout Central America. This song is ideal for times of response within corporate worship.

34 ENTONEMOS UN CANTO DE ALABANZA
Let us sing to the Lord a song of praise

GUATEMALA

Words: unknown
translated G. Lockwood
in this version Word & Music
Music: Alfredo Colom
arranged Christopher Norton

Lively ♩ = 125

1 En-to - ne-mos un can-to de a-la - ban-za en-to - ne-mos un cán-ti-co al Se -
1 Let us sing to the Lord a song of praise, let us raise all our voi-ces to the

-ñor___ en-to - ne-mos sal-mo-dias ce - les - tia - les en-to -
Lord,___ let us sing psalms of glo-ry to the Sa-viour, let us

- ne-mos mil cán - ti - cos de a-mor;_ en-to - ne - mos sal-mo-dias ce - les -
join in a thou-sand songs of love;_ let us sing psalms of glo-ry to the

- tia - les en-to - ne - mos mil cán - ti - cos de a-mor.
Sa - viour, let us join in a thou-sand songs of love.

A lively dance song which seems to cry out for guitars and light percussion accompaniment.
Don't be afraid to experiment with descants and harmonies.

1 *Entonemos un canto de alabanza*
entonemos un cántico al Señor
entonemos salmodias celestiales
entonemos mil cánticos de amor;
   entonemos salmodias . . .

2 *Demos gracias al Padre por la vida,*
demos gracias al Padre por Jesús.
Y sigamos la senda de la gloria
con la carga divina de la cruz;
   y sigamos la senda . . .

3 *Demos gloria al Señor por este dia*
por sus muchos cuidados, por su amor
porque Dios en su gran misericordia
nos dio vida en Jesús nuestro Señor;
   porque Dios . . .

1 Let us sing to the Lord a song of praise,
let us raise all our voices to the Lord,
let us sing psalms of glory to the Saviour,
let us join in a thousand songs of love;
   let us sing psalms of glory . . .

2 Thanks we give for the gift of life you grant us,
thanks we give to our God for Jesus Christ –
so let's follow the path that leads to glory,
with the glorious burden of the cross;
   so let's follow . . .

3 Let us take to ourselves the heavenly armour,
let us use all love's weapons in our cause;
we will fight for the right, till in the future
we can say, 'We are more than conquerors!'
   we will fight . . .

4 Glory give to our God for each new morning,
for his wonderful blessings and his love:
for our God in the goodness of his mercy
gave us life, life in Jesus Christ our Lord;
   for our God . . .

35 FOOD TO PILGRIMS

KOREA

After Geonyong Lee
in this version Word & Music
Music: Geonyong Lee
arranged Geoff Weaver

1 Food to pil-grims giv - en, strength up - on the way;
2 Streams of grace are flow - ing — life from death for me;
3 I re - ceive your bless - ing — Jes - us, king div - ine;

bread come down from hea - ven — Christ is ours to - day!
truth and good-ness grow - ing for e - ter - ni - ty.
all your love con - fess - ing in this bread and wine.

Feed us now, O Lord, with this ho - ly food —
Cleanse my soul, O Lord, with your pre - cious blood —
Send me out, O Lord, ho - ly, pure and good,

> A haunting song, suitable for the Eucharist, from one of Korea's leading composers, Geonyong Lee. Ideally this should be sung unaccompanied.

let your king-dom come, O Lord, let your king - dom come;
let your will be done, O Lord, let your will be done;
till the world is won, O Lord, till the world is won;

let your king-dom come, O Lord, let your king - dom come.
let your will be done, O Lord, let your will be done.
till the world is won, O Lord, till the world is won.

1 Food to pilgrims given,
   strength upon the way;
   bread come down from heaven –
   Christ is ours today!
   Feed us now, O Lord, with this holy food –
   let your kingdom come, O Lord, let your kingdom come;
   let your kingdom come, O Lord, let your kingdom come.

2 Streams of grace are flowing –
   life from death for me;
   truth and goodness growing
   for eternity.
   Cleanse my soul, O Lord, with your precious blood –
   let your will be done, O Lord, let your will be done;
   let your will be done, O Lord, let your will be done.

3 I receive your blessing –
   Jesus, king divine;
   all your love confessing
   in this bread and wine.
   Send me out, O Lord, holy, pure and good,
   till the world is won, O Lord, till the world is won;
   till the world is won, O Lord, till the world is won.

36 FOR THE BEAUTY OF THE EARTH

CHINA

MO-LI-HUA

Words: F. Sandford Pierpoint
Music: Chinese folk song
adapted I-to-Loh

Worshipfully ♩ = 80

1 For the beau-ty_ of the earth, for the beau-ty_ of the skies,
2 For the beau-ty_ of each hour of the day and of the night,
3 For the joy of_ ear and eye, for the heart and mind's de-light,

for the love which from our birth o - ver_ and a -
hill and vale, and_ tree and flower, sun and moon and_
for the my - stic_ har - mo - ny link - ing_ sense to_

- round us_ lies,
stars of_ light,   Christ our God,   to you we_ raise
sound and sight,

This lovely Chinese folk song, used by Puccini in his opera 'Turandot', is a song about
flowers. It is appropriate therefore that it should be sung as a hymn of thanksgiving for
God's creation. Be particularly sensitive to the ebb and flow of the phrases.

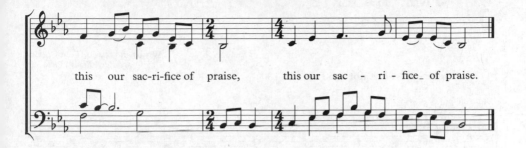

this our sac-ri-fice of praise, this our sac - ri - fice_ of praise.

1 For the beauty of the earth,
for the beauty of the skies,
for the love which from our birth
over and around us lies,
    Christ our God, to you we raise
    this our sacrifice of praise,
    this our sacrifice of praise.

2 For the beauty of each hour
of the day and of the night,
hill and vale, and tree and flower,
sun and moon and stars of light,
    Christ our God . . .

3 For the joy of ear and eye,
for the heart and mind's delight,
for the mystic harmony
linking sense to sound and sight,
    Christ our God . . .

4 For the joy of human love,
brother, sister, parent, child,
friends on earth and friends above,
pleasures pure and undefiled,
    Christ our God . . .

5 For each perfect gift divine
to our race so freely given,
joys bestowed by love's design,
flowers of earth and fruits of heaven,
    Christ our God . . .

37 FREE TO SERVE

GHANA

Words and music: Tom Colvin
arranged David Peacock

Confidently, but not too fast ♩ = 100

Chorus

Free to serve, yes, free to serve, Christ has set us___ free___

___ to serve; free to serve, yes, free to serve, all in Christ are_ free

Fine Verse

___ to serve.
1 When we walk a-lone and we work for self, when we
2 But that lone-ly road leads to sla-ve-ry— life is
3 Ev-ery pass-er-by is a friend to love, ev-ery

make our plans just to in-crease our wealth; need-y neigh-bours there by the
full of fear, the end we can-not see; Christ has set us free, he has
one in need, some-one in Christ to serve; fair so-ci-e-ty, hu-man

Singers may follow the three-part harmony as scored.

A Ghanaian melody which in its directness and its syncopated rhythms captures the joy of freedom.
A drum accompaniment will help to give the music an authentically Ghanaian flavour.

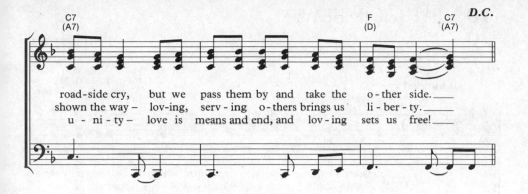

road-side cry, but we pass them by and take the o - ther side. ___
shown the way – lov-ing, serv - ing o - thers brings us li - ber - ty. ___
u – ni - ty – love is means and end, and lov - ing sets us free! ___

Free to serve, yes, free to serve,
Christ has set us free to serve;
free to serve, yes, free to serve,
all in Christ are free to serve.

1   When we walk alone and we work for self,
    when we make our plans just to increase our wealth;
    needy neighbours there by the roadside cry,
    but we pass them by and take the other side.
        Free to serve . . .

2   But that lonely road leads to slavery –
    life is full of fear, the end we cannot see;
    Christ has set us free, he has shown the way –
    loving, serving others brings us liberty.
        Free to serve . . .

3   Every passer-by is a friend to love,
    every one in need, someone in Christ to serve;
    fair society, human unity –
    love is means and end, and loving sets us free!
        Free to serve . . .

38 FATHER IN HEAVEN

PHILIPPINES

Words: D. T. Niles
Music: Elena G. Maquiso
arranged Geoff Weaver

HALAD

Unhurried ♩ = 88

1 Fa-ther in hea - ven,___ grant to your chil - dren___ mer - cy and
(2) - deem - er,___ may we re - mem - ber___ your gra-cious
(3) - cend - ing,___ whose is the bless - ing,___ strength for the

bless - ing,___ songs ne - ver ceas - ing;___ love to u -
pas - sion,___ your re - sur - rec - tion:___ wor - ship we
wea - ry,___ help for the nee - dy:___ seal - ing Christ's

- nite us,___ grace to re - deem us,___ Fa - ther in
bring you,___ praise we shall sing you,___ Je - sus re -
Lord - ship,___ bless - ing our wor - ship,___ Spi - rit des -

hea - ven,___ Fa - ther, our God. 2 Je - sus re -
- deem - er,___ Je - sus, our Lord. 3 Spi - rit des -
- cend - ing, Spi - rit a - - dored.

A beautiful hymn to the Trinity based on a Filipino folk song.
The words are by D. T. Niles, the great Sri Lankan Christian leader.

39 GET TOGETHER

CARIBBEAN

Words: unknown
Music: Caribbean melody
arranged Geoff Weaver

Rhythmically ♩ = 108

Get to-geth-er, get to-geth-er, get to-geth-er in the Lord. Let us
all get to-geth-er in the Lord; (in the Lord) let us greet one a-no-ther as
sis - ter and bro-ther –let us all get to-geth-er in the Lord.

An ideal song, simple and rhythmic, for the exchanging of the Peace. The editor was literally 'caught up' while singing this song at a service in Birmingham Cathedral where the predominantly black congregation welcomed Archbishop Desmond Tutu.

40 GABI, GABI
Praise the Father

Words: collected and edited by Anders Nyberg
Music: African melody, scored by Notman KB,
Ljungsbro and Lars Parkman

Strongly rhythmic ♩ = 116

Capo 1(G)

Ga - bi, Ga - bi,   bash' ab - az - al -
Praise   the   Fa - ther,   li - be - ra - tor,

Ga - bi, Ga - bi,   Ga - bi, Ga - bi,
Praise the Fa - ther,   praise the Fa - ther,

Ga - bi,   Ga - bi,   bash' ab - az - al -
Praise the   Fa-ther,   li - be - ra - tor,

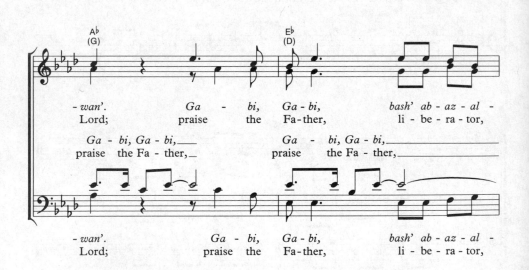

- wan'.   Ga - bi, Ga - bi,   bash' ab - az - al -
Lord;   praise the Fa - ther,   li - be - ra - tor,

Ga - bi, Ga - bi,   Ga - bi, Ga - bi,
praise the Fa - ther,   praise the Fa - ther,

- wan'.   Ga - bi, Ga - bi,   bash' ab - az - al -
Lord;   praise the Fa-ther,   li - be - ra - tor,

> A joyful song of liberation from South Africa, once sung in hope, now in
> thanksgiving. The repeated tenor phrase should be both prominent and
> rhythmic, and ideally the song should be sung unaccompanied.

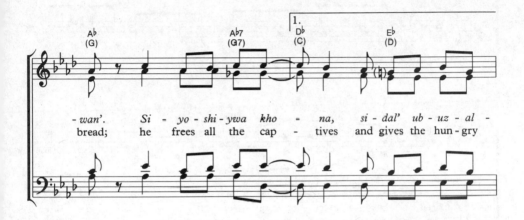

41 GINOO MALOOY KA KANAMO
O Lord, have mercy

PHILIPPINES

KYRIE

Words: traditional
Music: as taught by Jeaneth Harris
arranged Geoff Weaver

With quiet intensity ♩ = 76

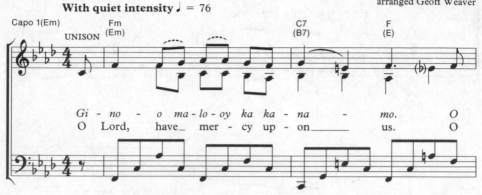

Gi - no - o ma-lo-oy ka ka-na - mo. O
O Lord, have mer - cy up - on us. O

Cri - sto ma-lo-oy ka ka-na - mo. Gi -
Christ, have mer - cy up - on us. O

-no - o ma-lo-oy ka ka-na - mo.
Lord, have mer - cy up - on us.

A haunting, melancholy Kyrie (Lord, have mercy) from the Philippines,
where so many people cry out in their sufferings and hardships.

HARMONY

Gi - no - o ma - lo - oy ka ka - na - mo. O
O Lord, have mer - cy up - on us. O

Cri - sto ma - lo - oy ka ka - na - mo. Gi -
Christ, have mer - cy up - on us. O

-no - o ma - lo - oy ka ka - na - mo.
Lord, have mer - cy up - on us.

Ginoo malooy ka kanamo.
O Cristo malooy ka kanamo.
Ginoo malooy ka kanamo.

O Lord, have mercy upon us.
O Christ, have mercy upon us.
O Lord, have mercy upon us.

42 GLORY TO GOD

PERU

Words and music: unknown

Lively but not too quickly ♩ = 132

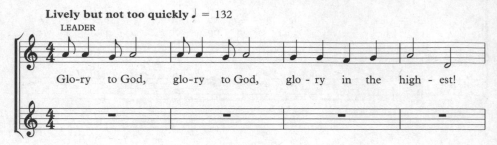

LEADER

Glo-ry to God, glo-ry to God, glo - ry in the high - est!

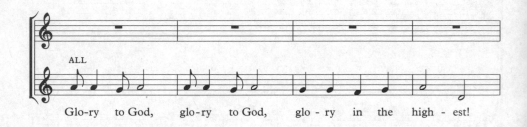

ALL

Glo-ry to God, glo-ry to God, glo - ry in the high - est!

To God be glo-ry for ev - er!

To God be glo-ry for ev - er!

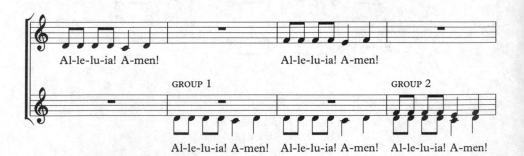

Al-le-lu-ia! A-men! Al-le-lu-ia! A-men!

GROUP 1

GROUP 2

Al-le-lu-ia! A-men! Al-le-lu-ia! A-men! Al-le-lu-ia! A-men!

> This is ideal for celebrations and for any festive occasion. There are
> many ways of performing the Alleluias— feel free to experiment and to
> extend them. The song should be rhythmic but not too quick.

Al-le-lu-ia! A-men!

GROUP 3

Al-le-lu-ia! A-men! Al-le-lu-ia! A-men! Al-le-lu-ia! A-men! Al-le-lu-ia! A-men!_

LEADER	Glory to God, glory to God, glory in the highest!
ALL	Glory to God, glory to God, glory in the highest!
LEADER	To God be glory for ever!
ALL	To God be glory for ever!
LEADER	Alleluia! Amen!
GROUP I	Alleluia! Amen!
LEADER	Alleluia! Amen!
GROUPS I, 2	Alleluia! Amen!
LEADER	Alleluia! Amen!
GROUPS I, 2, 3	Alleluia! Amen!
ALL	Alleluia! Amen! Alleluia! Amen!

43 GLORIA, GLORIA, GLORIA
Glory, glory, glory

ARGENTINA

Music: Pablo D. Sosa

Glo - ria, glo - ria, glo - ria en las al - tur - as a Dios!
Glo - ry, glo - ry, glo - ry, glo - ry be to God on high!

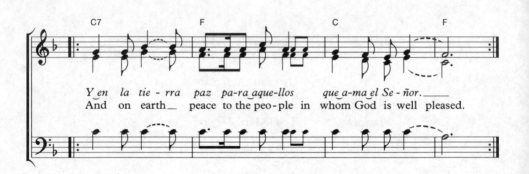

Y en la tie - rra paz pa - ra aque - llos que a - ma el Se - ñor.____
And on earth__ peace to the peo - ple in whom God is well pleased.

Gloria, gloria, gloria	Glory, glory, glory,
en las alturas a Dios!	glory be to God on high!
Gloria . . .	Glory . . .
Y en la tierra paz para aquellos	And on earth peace to the people
que ama el Señor.	in whom God is well pleased.
Y en la tierra . . .	And on earth . . .

Pablo Sosa is an Argentinian pastor and a prolific composer of new worship songs, often making use of folk dance rhythms and idioms. This Gloria uses the alternating §¾ of the cueca, one of the national dances of Argentina, in recent times danced by women whose husbands have 'disappeared'. It should be sung lightly, rhythmically and unaccompanied, with a light percussion accompaniment.

44 GLORIA, GLORIA
Glory to God

Words: traditional
Music: Jacques Berthier

CANON

Glo - ri - a,   glo - ri - a,   in ex - cel - sis De - o!
Glo-ry to God,   glo-ry to God,   glo - ry in___ the high - est!

Glo - ri - a,   glo - ri - a,   al - le - lu - ia,   al - le - lu - ia!
Glo-ry to God,   glo-ry to God,   al - le - lu - ia,   al - le - lu - ia!

KEYBOARD OR INSTRUMENTS

This item may be sung as an unaccompanied four-part canon.

45 GLORY TO THE LORD OF LOVE
Ay Ay Salidumay

Words: from Luke 1 (Magnificat), Michael Perry
Music: based on a Kalinga melody, Henry Kiley
arranged Geoff Weaver

Simply ♩ = 66

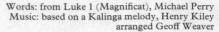

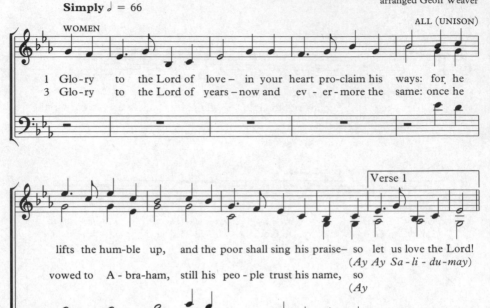

WOMEN / ALL (UNISON)

1 Glo-ry to the Lord of love – in your heart pro-claim his ways: for he
3 Glo-ry to the Lord of years – now and ev-er-more the same: once he

Verse 1

lifts the hum-ble up, and the poor shall sing his praise– so let us love the Lord!
(Ay Ay Sa-li-du-may)
vowed to A-bra-ham, still his peo-ple trust his name, so
(Ay

Verse 2   SOLO INSTRUMENT

ALL

2 Glo-ry to the Lord of life – he has shown his might-y

deeds: with his arm he slays the proud, with his

A pentatonic melody, based on a Filipino folksong, which seems ideal for conveying the simple trust of Mary's response. For Filipino Christians this song is not just about Mary's response. It is also about the God who 'slays the proud and lifts up the humble and the poor'. It should ideally be sung unaccompanied. In the final phrase of each verse, the Filipino may be substituted for the English.

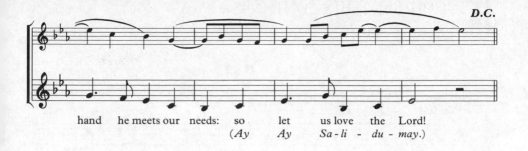

hand he meets our needs: so let us love the Lord!
(Ay Ay Sa - li - du - may.)

Verse 3

let us praise, so let us praise, so let us praise the Lord!
(Ay Sa - li - du - may, Sa - li - du - may, Sa - li - du - may)

1 WOMEN Glory to the Lord of love –
in your heart proclaim his ways:
ALL for he lifts the humble up,
and the poor shall sing his praise –
so let us love the Lord!
(Ay Ay Salidumay)

2 ALL Glory to the Lord of life –
he has shown his mighty deeds:
with his arm he slays the proud,
with his hand he meets our needs:
so let us thank the Lord!
(Ay Ay Salidumay)

3 WOMEN Glory to the Lord of years –
now and evermore the same:
ALL once he vowed to Abraham,
still his people trust his name,
so let us praise,
so let us praise,
so let us praise the Lord!
(Ay Ay Salidumay)

46 GOD SENT HIS SON
Nanti ithemba

ZIMBABWE

Words: from the African
Geoff Weaver
Music: unknown
arranged Joseph Kiwele

Lively ♩ = 120

Verse

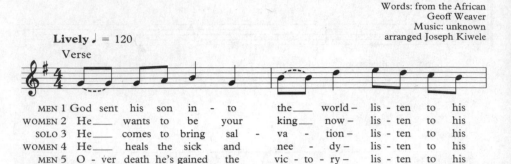

MEN 1 God sent his son in - to the ___ world – lis - ten to his
WOMEN 2 He ___ wants to be your king ___ now – lis - ten to his
SOLO 3 He ___ comes to bring sal - va - tion – lis - ten to his
WOMEN 4 He ___ heals the sick and nee - dy – lis - ten to his
MEN 5 O - ver death he's gained the vic - to - ry – lis - ten to his

voice to - day; hear of his sal - va - tion com - ing, hur - ry, go and
voice to - day; mer - cy and ___ bless - ing he will give to you to -
voice to - day; he brings free - dom, joy and health to all his faith - ful
voice to - day; he, the Bread of Life, gives bread to all who come in
voice to - day; by his death and rais - ing up we too have gained new

tell it. ___ All you Christ - ians hear!
- day. ___ All you Christ - ians hear!
peo - ple. ___ All you Christ - ians hear!
need. ___ All you Christ - ians hear!
life to - day. ___ All you Christ - ians hear!

Chorus

ALL Sing hal - le - lu - jah, night is gone; ___ let us re - joice, the

Sing hal - le - lu - jah, night is gone; ___

> An exuberant Advent or Christmas song from Zimbabwe.
> It should be unaccompanied and with lively drum accompaniment.

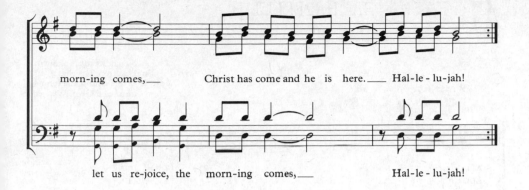

morn-ing comes,___ Christ has come and he is here.___ Hal-le - lu-jah!

let us re-joice, the morn-ing comes,___ Hal-le - lu-jah!

1 MEN   God sent his son into the world –
listen to his voice today;
hear of his salvation coming,
    hurry, go and tell it.
All you Christians hear!

ALL   Sing hallelujah, night is gone;
let us rejoice, the morning comes,
Christ has come and he is here.
Hallelujah!

2 WOMEN   He wants to be your king now –
listen to his voice today;
mercy and blessing
    he will give to you today.
All you Christians hear!

ALL   Sing hallelujah, night is gone . . .

3 SOLO   He comes to bring salvation –
listen to his voice today;
he brings freedom, joy and health
    to all his faithful people.
All you Christians hear!

ALL   Sing hallelujah, night is gone . . .

4 WOMEN   He heals the sick and needy –
listen to his voice today;
he, the Bread of Life, gives bread
    to all who come in need.
All you Christians hear!

ALL   Sing hallelujah, night is gone . . .

5 MEN   Over death he's gained the victory –
listen to his voice today;
by his death and raising up
    we too have gained new life today.
All you Christians hear!

ALL   Sing hallelujah, night is gone . . .

47 HA- HA- HA- HALELLUIAH

NEPAL

Nepali words: unknown
English: from Revelation 19
Word & Music / Jubilate Hymns
arranged Geoff Weaver

A song of great conviction from the rapidly growing Christian community in Nepal.
The waltz rhythm should be well marked throughout.

48 HALLE, HALLE, HALLELUJAH

CARIBBEAN

Words: traditional
Music: unknown
arranged Geoff Weaver

A song from the Caribbean, where many people are uninhibited in expressing their worship.

Music arrangement: © 1993 Geoff Weaver / Jubilate Hymns

49 HALELUYA! PELO TSA RONA
Alleluia! We sing your praises

SOUTH AFRICA

Words: African origin
collected and edited by Anders Nyberg
Music: African melody
scored by Notman KB, Ljungsbro
and Lars Parkman

An astonishing wealth of song has come out of South Africa in recent years. Songs of pain and protest, but also songs of faith and hope such as this one. The syncopated rhythms should be strongly marked.

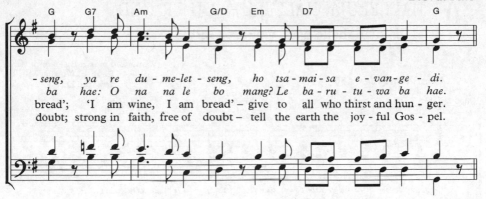

-seng, ya re du - me-let - seng, ho tsa - mai - sa e - van - ge - di.
ba hae: O na na le bo mang? Le ba - ru - tu - wa ba hae.
bread'; 'I am wine, I am bread' – give to all who thirst and hun - ger.
doubt; strong in faith, free of doubt – tell the earth the joy - ful Gos - pel.

Haleluya! Pelo tsa rona,
di thabile kaofela.
Haleluya . . .

1 *Ke Morena Jeso,*
ya re dumeletseng,
ya re dumeletseng,
ho tsamaisa evangedi.
Haleluya . . .

2 *O na na le bo mang?*
Le barutuwa ba hae:
O na na le bo mang?
Le barutuwa ba hae.
Haleluya . . .

Alleluia!
We sing your praises,
all our hearts
are filled with gladness.
Alleluia . . .

1 Christ the Lord to us said,
'I am wine, I am bread';
'I am wine, I am bread' –
give to all who thirst and hunger.
Alleluia . . .

2 Now he sends us all out,
strong in faith, free of doubt;
strong in faith, free of doubt –
tell the earth the joyful Gospel.
Alleluia . . .

50 HALLELUJA, HALLELUJA DU ER GUD

Hallelujah, hallelujah, you are God

NORWAY

Words and music: Eva Konradsen
English: Word & Music
arranged David Peacock

1 Hal - le - lu - ja, hal - le - lu - ja__ du er__ Gud.__
2 Hal - le - lu - ja, hal - le - lu - ja__ du er__ Far.__
1 Hal - le - lu - jah, hal - le - lu - jah,__ you are__ God,__
2 Hal - le - lu - jah, hal - le - lu - jah,__ you are__ Fa - ther,

Hal - le - lu - ja, hal - le - lu - ja__ du er__ Gud._
Hal - le - lu - ja, hal - le - lu - ja__ du er__ Far._
hal - le - lu - jah, hal - le - lu - jah,__ you are__ God;
hal - le - lu - jah, hal - le - lu - jah,__ you are__ Fa -

_____ Du er rik på mis - kunn - het,__
_____ Du er rik på tro - fast - het;__
_____ you are full of gent - le - ness
- ther;_____ you are full of faith - ful - ness

This item is one of the recent worship songs being composed
and increasingly used within Scandinavian churches.

	C (A)	B♭/C (G)	F (D)	F/A	B♭maj7 (G)

_ og din nå - de va - rer__ ved.__ Hal - le -
_ og din om - sorg va - rer__ ved.__ Hal - le -
_ and your grace is with - out__ end,__ hal - le -
_ and your care is with - out__ end,__ hal - le -

Gm (Em)		Am7 (F♯m)		Dm (Bm)

- lu - ja, hal - le - lu - ja__ du er__ Gud._____
- lu - ja, hal - le - lu - ja__ du er__ Far._____
- lu - jah, hal - le - lu - jah,_ you are__ God._____
- lu - jah, hal - le - lu - jah,_ you are__ Fa - ther.____

1   *Halleluja, halleluja du er Gud.*
   Halleluja, halleluja du er Gud.
    Du er rik på miskunnhet,
    og din nåde varer ved.
   Halleluja, halleluja du er Gud.

2   *Halleluja, halleluja du er Far.*
   Halleluja, halleluja du er Far.
    Du er rik på trofasthet;
    og din omsorg varer ved.
   Halleluja, halleluja du er Far.

3   *Halleluja, halleluja Hellig Ånd.*
   Halleluja, halleluja Hellig Ånd.
    Du er rik på liv og kraft;
    utav intet gjør du alt.
   Halleluja, halleluja Hellig Ånd.

4   *Halleluja din er æren, Jesus Krist.*
   Halleluja din er æren, Jesus Krist.
    Ved din død på Golgata
    fikk jeg liv, halleluja.
   Halleluja din er æren, Jesus Krist.

1   Hallelujah, hallelujah, you are God,
   hallelujah, hallelujah, you are God;
    you are full of gentleness
    and your grace is without end,
   hallelujah, hallelujah, you are God.

2   Hallelujah, hallelujah, you are Father,
   hallelujah, hallelujah, you are Father;
    you are full of faithfulness
    and your care is without end,
   hallelujah, hallelujah, you are Father.

3   Hallelujah, hallelujah, Holy Spirit,
   hallelujah, hallelujah, Holy Spirit;
    you are full of life and power;
    you are wind of heaven's breath,
   hallelujah, hallelujah, Holy Spirit.

4   Hallelujah, glory be to Jesus Christ,
   hallelujah, glory be to Jesus Christ:
    by your death on Calvary
    I found life and hope and love –
   hallelujah, glory be to Jesus Christ.

51 HALLELUJAH

ZIMBABWE

Words: traditional
Music: Abraham Maraire

Dynamically ♩. = 66

Hal - le - lu - jah,_____ hal - le - lu - jah,

Hal - le - lu - jah, hal - le - lu -,

Hal - le - lu - jah, hal - le - lu - jah,

hal - le - lu - jah,_____ hal - le - lu - jah!

hal - le - lu - jah, hal - le - lu - jah!

hal - le - lu - jah, hal - le - lu - jah!

An exuberant outburst, ideal as a congregational response before and after the Gospel reading. It moves quickly, effectively one beat to a bar.

52 HAMBA NATHI
Come walk with us

SOUTH AFRICA

Words: edited by Anders Nyberg
Music: African melody, scored by Notman KB,
Ljungsbro and Lars Parkman

With rhythmic freedom ♩ = 80

Like so many African songs, this is cast in a leader-response format.
Feel the rhythms rather than counting them.

1.
2.
D.S.

2   LEADER   *Theta nathi*
       ALL   *Theta nathi mkululu wethu*
       LEADER   *Theta nathi*
       ALL   *Theta nathi mkululu wethu*
       LEADER   *Theta nathi . . .*

         LEADER   *mkululu wethu*
         ALL   *mkululu, mkululu, mkululu wethu . . .*

2   LEADER   Listen to us,
       ALL   listen to us – our hearts are heavy.
       LEADER   Listen to us,
       ALL   listen to us – our hearts are heavy.
       LEADER   Listen to us . . .

         LEADER   O Lord our God,
         ALL   O Lord, O Lord, O Lord our God . . .

OTHER VERSES

3   LEADER   Come walk with us,
       ALL   come walk with us, the road is so long . . .

4   LEADER   Talk with us,
       ALL   talk with us, O Lord our God . . .

53 HANÚRE BINNANÚN
Star of the morning

KOREA

Words: after Reginald Heber
translated Marion Kim and James Minchin
adapted Word & Music
Music: Un-yung La

With quiet simplicity ♩ = 88

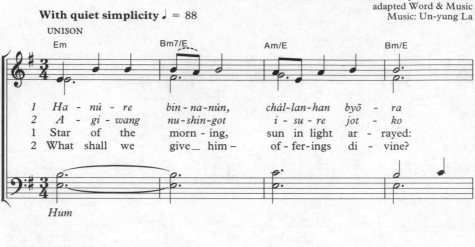

1 Ha - nú - re   bin - na - nún,   chál - lan - han   byõ - ra
2 A - gi - wang   nu - shin - got   i - su - re   jot - ko
1 Star of the   morn - ing,   sun in light   ar - rayed:
2 What shall we   give_ him –   of - fer-ings   di - vine?

Hum

u - ri - ui   õ - dun - gil   bal - ki - õ - ra
jim - sung - gwa   han - ga - ji   nu - u - shot - da
dawn on our   dark - ness,   come to our   aid –
Gems from the   moun - tain,   gold from the   mine?

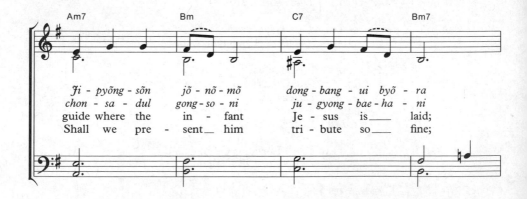

Ji - pyõng - sõn   jõ - nõ - mõ   dong - bang - ui byõ - ra
chon - sa - dul   gong - so - ni   ju - gyong - bae - ha - ni
guide where the   in - fant   Je - sus is_ laid;
Shall we pre - sent_ him   tri - bute so_ fine;

This charming Korean carol has a folk-like simplicity, and would lend itself well to instrumental accompaniment – glockenspiels and bells would add an appropriate touch of colour.

Under the music, the lyrics:

a - gi - kke   u - ri - rul   in - do - ha - ra.
im - gum - gwa   gu - ju - wa   chang - jo - ju - ra.
guide where the   in - fant   Je - sus is laid.
shall we pre - sent_ him   tri - bute so fine?

1 Hanúre binnanún, chállanhan byõra
   uriui õdungil balkiõra.
   Jipyõngsõn jõnõmõ dongbangui byõra
   agikke urirul indohara.

2 Agiwang nushingot isure jotko
   jimsunggwa hangaji nuushotda
   chonsadul gongsoni jugyongbaehani
   imgumgwa gujuwa changjojura.

3 Urinun ottoke jungsongul boelkka
   hyanggiron jemurul bach'iolkka
   jo sanui yuhyanggwa badaui ch' inju
   hwanggumgwa moryagul bach' iolkka.

4 Kappissan yemurul durindahaedo
   junimul kipuge motanani
   junimi badushil ch' amdaun yemul
   jongsongdoen yebaewa gidoroda.

1 Star of the morning,
        sun in light arrayed:
   dawn on our darkness,
        come to our aid –
   guide where the infant
        Jesus is laid;
   guide where the infant
        Jesus is laid.

2 What shall we give him –
        offerings divine?
   Gems from the mountain,
        gold from the mine?
   Shall we present him
        tribute so fine;
   shall we present him
        tribute so fine?

3 Vainly we offer,
        favours to secure,
   such costly presents –
        but these endure:
   faith's adoration,
        prayers of the poor;
   faith's adoration,
        prayers of the poor.

4 Star of the morning . . .

54 HAVE YOU EVER SEEN

PAKISTAN

Words: Narayan Vaman Tilak (Marathi)
translated Nicol Macnicol (adapted)
Music: Urdu melody
arranged Geoff Weaver

With feeling ♩ = 76

Capo 1(D)

1 Have you ev - er seen the Lord, Christ the cru - ci - fied? Have you
2 Have you seen your-self in them – one who hurt him so? Have you
3 Have you seen how he, to save, suf - fers there and dies? Have you

seen those wound-ed hands? Have you seen his side? Have you
seen the sin - ner who caused your sav - iour's woe? Have you
seen on whom he looks with his lov - ing eyes? Have you

seen the cru - el thorns, wo - ven for a crown? Have you,
seen the cloak of night which dark Cal - vary wore? Have you
ev - er, ev - er seen love so deep as this? Have you

A haunting Urdu song inviting the listener to contemplate the sufferings of Christ,
and to respond with self-offering. Be aware of the growing intensity of the phrase
through the repeated melodic notes.

1 Have you ever seen the Lord,
  Christ the crucified?
Have you seen those wounded hands?
  Have you seen his side?
Have you seen the cruel thorns,
  woven for a crown?
Have you, have you seen his blood,
  dropping, dropping down?
Have you seen the cruel thorns . . .

2 Have you seen yourself in them –
  one who hurt him so?
Have you seen the sinner who
  caused your saviour's woe?
Have you seen the cloak of night
  which dark Calvary wore?
Have you seen a loneliness
  such as Jesus bore?
Have you seen the cloak of night . . .

3 Have you seen how he, to save,
  suffers there and dies?
Have you seen on whom he looks
  with his loving eyes?
Have you ever, ever seen
  love so deep as this?
Have you given up your life
  wholly to be his?
Have you ever, ever seen . . .

55 HAY MOMENTOS
There are moments

ARGENTINA

Words: unknown
translated Dina de Carro
Music: unknown
arranged David Peacock

Hay mo - men - tos, que las pa - la - bras no al -
There are mo - ments when words can - not ex - press com -

- can - zan, pa - ra de - cir - te lo que sien - to
- plete - ly all the feel - ings that my heart can hold

1.
por ti mi buen Se - ñor. Hay mo -
for you my God and Lord. There are

2.
por ti mi buen Se - ñor. Yo te a - gra -
for you my God and Lord. And I will

A popular worship song which is used throughout Central America.

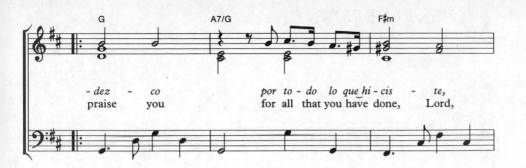

-dez - co / por to-do lo que hi-cis - te,
praise you / for all that you have done, Lord,

por to - do lo que ha - ces,
for all that you are do - ing,

1.

y to-do lo que ha-rás.
for all that you will do.

Yo te a-gra-
And I will

2.

y to - do lo que ha - rás.____
for all that you will do.____

56 HE CAME DOWN

CAMEROON

Words and music: unknown
arranged Geoff Weaver

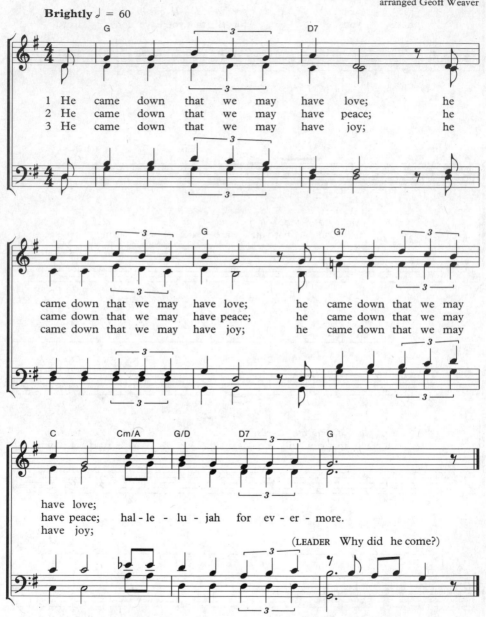

Brightly ♩ = 60

1 He came down that we may have love; he
2 He came down that we may have peace; he
3 He came down that we may have joy; he

came down that we may have love; he came down that we may
came down that we may have peace; he came down that we may
came down that we may have joy; he came down that we may

have love;
have peace; hal - le - lu - jah for ev - er - more.
have joy;

(LEADER Why did he come?)

4   He came down that we may have power . . .

5   He came down that we may have hope . . .

> A traditional Cameroonian song, which is often performed as a circle
> dance with sweeping movements to suggest Christ's coming down.
> The leader calls and encourages the congregation to respond.

57 HE WAS BORN A LITTLE CHILD

MALAWI

Words: from the Malawi
Helen Taylor
Music: unknown
arranged Geoff Weaver

Gently ♩ = 92
Verse

Capo 3(D)

1 He was born a lit-tle child when he came to earth;—
2 Shep-herds and their qui-et sheep saw the an-gel bright;—
3 In the hills they left the lambs and the sleep-ing sheep;—
4 'Shep-herds, you have run from a-far, breath-less, breath-less still:—
5 'Shall we not a-dore him, ly-ing in the hay?—

an-gels in the heavens a-bove told us of his birth.
shep-herds heard the an-gels sing-ing in the night.
down to Beth-le-hem they came, Je-sus Christ to seek.
who is car-ing for your sheep on the star-lit hill?'
Look, our sav-iour Je-sus, born for us to-day!'

Chorus

Mo-ther Ma-ry laid him in a cat-tle stall—

lit-tle ba-by Je-sus who was Lord of all.

> A gentle carol from Malawi, ideally sung unaccompanied.
> Note the pentatonic (5 note scale) structure of the melody.

Words and music: unknown
Music arranged David Peacock

Lively ♩ = 120

He is ris-en,— ris-en,— ris-en;— he is
(ris-en) (ris-en) (ris-en)

ris-en,— ris-en – the Lord: he is Lord!
(ris-en, ris-en – the Lord:) Lord!)

LEADER   ALL
1 Oh be joy-ful–
2 O-ver death's power Je-
3 Al-le-lu-ia! All

1 join in praise and sing:_____ O al-le-lu-
2 -sus has o-ver-come:_____ O al-le-lu-
3 Christ-ians, join us now:_____ O al-le-lu-

LEADER   ALL
-ia! We were all dead; we now live in Je-sus:_ O
-ia! Life e-ter-nal Je-sus has giv-en us:_ O
-ia! He's tri-um-phant! All Christ-ians, praise him now,_ O

> Of uncertain origin, this song has many of the hallmarks of Africa – a leader
> calling for a response and lively rhythms to celebrate Christ's resurrection.

al - le - lu - ia! He is
al - le - lu - ia! He is
al - le - lu - - ia! Al - le -

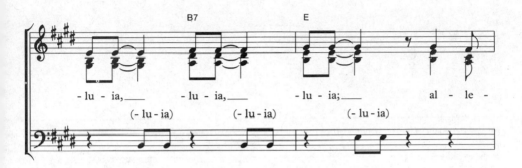

- lu - ia, ___ - lu - ia, ___ - lu - ia; ___ al - le -
(- lu - ia) (- lu - ia) (- lu - ia)

- lu - ia __ life is come: he is ris - en, __ ris - en, __
(- lu - ia life is come:) (ris-en) (ris-en)

ris - en; __ he is ris - en, __ ris - en _ the Lord!
(ris-en) (ris-en: ris - en _ the Lord!)

59 HEME AQUÍ
Here I am

MEXICO

Words: Marcos Witt
translated Word & Music
Music: Marcos Witt
arranged David Peacock

Worshipfully ♩ = 95

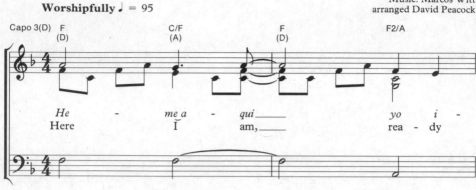

He - me a - qui___ yo i -
Here I am,___ rea - dy

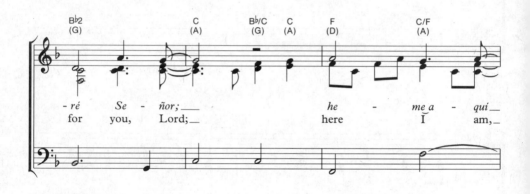

-ré Se - ñor;___ he - me a - qui
for you, Lord;___ here I am,___

___ yo i - ré Se - ñor.___ En - to
___ rea - dy for you,___ Lord ___ to

> Marcos Witt's songs are increasingly used throughout Latin America.
> This is an ideal song for times of response.

-ví - a - me___ a mi, que dis -
go where you___ will send,___ and to

- pues - to es - toy,___ lle - va - ré___ tu Glo -
give my life___ to pro - claim your glo -

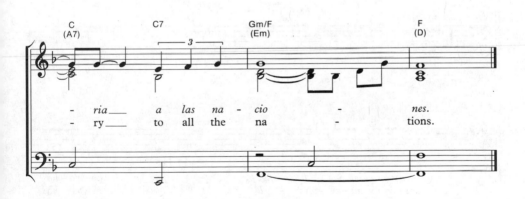

- ria___ a las na - cio - nes.
- ry___ to all the na - tions.

Heme aquí yo iré Señor;
heme aquí yo iré Señor.
Envíame a mi,
que dispuesto estoy,
llevaré tu Gloria a las naciones.

Here I am, ready for you, Lord;
here I am, ready for you, Lord –
to go where you will send,
and to give my life
to proclaim your glory to all the nations.

60 HINDI KO MAISIP
Far beyond our mind's grasp

PHILIPPINES

Words: after Francisco F. Feliciano
James Minchin
Music: based on 'Caturog na Nonoy'
arranged Geoff Weaver

With quiet joy ♩ = 132

INTRODUCTION

1 *Hin-di ko ma-i-sip,* kay la-king hi-wa-ga._____
2 *Ang a-bang ling-kod mo'y* di ka-ra-pat da-pat_____
1 Far be-yond our mind's grasp and our tongue's de-clar-ing,_____
2 None of us is wor-thy to re-ceive your es-sence_____

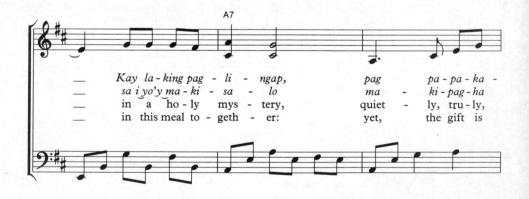

— *Kay la-king pag-li-ngap,* pag pa-pa-ka-
— *sa i yo'y ma-ki-sa-lo* ma-ki-pag-ha
— in a ho-ly mys-tery, quiet-ly, tru-ly,
— in this meal to-geth-er: yet, the gift is

An unusual combination of a Eucharistic text with a waltz-like Filipino folksong.
A guitar is the authentic instrument for accompaniment; if the piano is used,
there must be a strong rhythmic underlay.

Lyrics under the music (verses shown by line):

- sa - kit
pu - nan
you are here:
yours by choice;

sa - la ba-nubg ta - o
di na nag-na - na - is
lift - ed once on Cal - vary,
death can ne - ver snatch us

ng   i - yong a - ku - in
ng   ma - ra - ming ba - gay
sin   and weak-ness bear - ing,
from   your ho - ly pres - ence.

wa - lang hang -
sa - pat na
O Lord, how
Your pro - mise

- ga - nan Diyos, ang i yong pag-i - big.
ma - da - mang I - ka'y ka - pi - ling.
won - der - ful you call us to draw near!
is for life— we on - ly can re - joice.

- lan.
face.

3 Nang aking malasap alak at tinapay
   aking kagalakan ay walang mapagsidlan
   di kinakailangang akin pang wariin
   kung bakit ang ligaya ko'y walang patid.

4 Sana'y sa paglisan, sa Iyong tahanan
   aming mga puso ay Iyong lukuban
   na maging dambana ng iyong kabutihan
   maging huwaran ng pagmamahalan.

3 So our hearts are lifted to the realms above us,
   nourished and united by the precious bread and wine:
   here what sweet contentment, knowing that you love us!
   We thank you for this feast, this fellowship divine.

4 Soon you bid us scatter – share what we inherit –
   from this house of blessing where we taste your peace and grace.
   May our lives be altars glowing with your Spirit
   to light the lamps of those who also seek your face.

61 HOSANNA

ARGENTINA

Words: from Luke 19, unknown
Music: unknown
arranged David Peacock

Lively ♩ = 130

Ho - sa - nna,
Ho - san - na,

ho - sa - nna! Ho -
ho - san - na! Ho -

- sa - nna, ho - sa - nna!
- san - na, ho - san - na!

Ben - di - to se - a el Rey,
Bless - èd is the king,

A lively worship song which requires a strong rhythmic acccompaniment with a steady beat.

Hosanna, hosanna!
Hosanna, hosanna!
Bendito sea el Rey,
bendito sea el Rey,
bendito sea el Rey,
que viene en el nombre de Dios.

Hosanna, hosanna!
Hosanna, hosanna!
Blessed is the king,
blessed is the king,
blessed is the king
who comes in the name of the Lord!

62 HOSANNA, HOSANNA, HOSANNA

FRANCE

Words: traditional
Music: Jacques Berthier

Many who have gone to Taizé have been moved by the worship, with its use of repeated chants, which touch the depths of our being. A round or canon such as this enables a congregation to create harmony, giving an added dimension to their worship.

63 HOSANA, HOSANA

Hosanna, hosanna

ZIMBABWE

Words: after Abraham Maraire
Word & Music
Music: Abraham Maraire

Lively ♩ = 138

Chorus

Ho - sa - na, ho - sa - na! Ho-
Ho - san - na, ho - san - na, sing

OSTINATO

Come,_____ hur - ry now, come and see —

Fine

-sa - na Mwa - na wa - Mwa - ri!
praise to the Son___ of God!

yes,_____ Je - sus comes on the road

Verse *D.C.*

1 *Wo - pi - nda mu - Je - ru - sa - re - ma mu - sha wa - mwa - ri.*
1 Je - ru - sa - lem, Je - ru - sa - lem, a - rise to greet your king:
2 Make clear the way, the sav - iour comes, your palms and prais - es bring:
3 With bless - ings rise and hail the Lord, come, shout for joy and sing:

> An exuberant African welcome to Christ, ideal for a Palm Sunday procession.
> The rhythmic tenor and bass ostinato can be enhanced by other rhythmic patterns,
> e.g.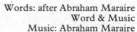
>
> During the verses, the men continue to sing the ostinato. However, it is suggested
> they are tacet for verse 2. Normally sung unaccompanied.

64 HWAYANA YA-MWARI
O Lamb of God

ZIMBABWE

AGNUS DEI

Words: traditional
Music: Emmanuel Ribeiro

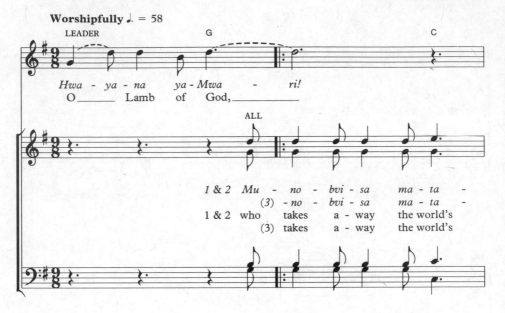

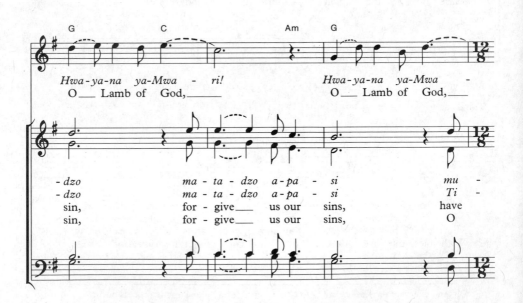

The traditional African leader-response pattern is used effectively in this beautiful song.

<table>
</table>

1	LEADER	*Hwayana ya-Mwari!*		1	LEADER	O Lamb of God,
	ALL	*Munobvisa matadzo*			ALL	who takes away the world's sin,
	LEADER	*Hwayana ya-Mwari!*			LEADER	O Lamb of God,
	ALL	*matadzo apasi*			ALL	forgive us our sins,
	LEADER	*Hwayana ya-Mwari!*			LEADER	O Lamb of God,
	ALL	*mutinzwi reiwo tsitsi!*			ALL	have mercy upon us, Lamb of God.

2	LEADER	*Hwayana ya-Mwari!*		2	LEADER	O Lamb of God,
	ALL	*Munobvisa matadzo*			ALL	who takes away the world's sin,
	LEADER	*Hwayana ya-Mwari!*			LEADER	O Lamb of God,
	ALL	*matadzo apasi*			ALL	forgive us our sins,
	LEADER	*Hwayana ya-Mwari!*			LEADER	O Lamb of God,
	ALL	*mutinzwi reiwo tsitsi!*			ALL	have mercy upon us, Lamb of God.

3	LEADER	*Hwayana ya-Mwari!*		3	LEADER	O Lamb of God,
	ALL	*Munobvisa matadzo*			ALL	who takes away the world's sin,
	LEADER	*Hwayana ya-Mwari!*			LEADER	O Lamb of God,
	ALL	*matadzo apasi*			ALL	forgive us our sins,
	LEADER	*Hwayana ya-Mwari!*			LEADER	O Lamb of God,
	ALL	*Tipeiwo rugare!*			ALL	O Jesus, grant us your peace.

65 HUMBLY IN YOUR SIGHT

MALAWI

Words and music: Tom Colvin
arranged Geoff Weaver

1 Hum - bly in your sight we come to - ge - ther, Lord:___
2 These our hearts are yours— we give them to you, Lord:___
3 These our ears are yours, we give them to you, Lord:___
4 These our eyes are yours, we give them to you, Lord:___

grant us now the bless - ing of your pre - sence here.
pu - ri - fy our love to make it like your own.
o - pen them to hear the gos - pel straight from you.
may we al - ways see this world as with your sight.

Alternative setting for verses 3 and 7.
Sopranos sing the words, lower voices hum

3 These our ears are yours, we give them to you, Lord:___
7 These our feet are yours, we give them to you, Lord:___

A simple Malawian folk song with straightforward harmonies,
effective when sung as people gather for worship

o - pen them to hear the gos - pel straight from you.
may we al - ways walk the path of light with you.

1 Humbly in your sight we come together, Lord:
  grant us now the blessing of your presence here.

2 These our hearts are yours – we give them to you, Lord:
  purify our love to make it like your own.

3 These our ears are yours, we give them to you, Lord:
  open them to hear the gospel straight from you.

4 These our eyes are yours, we give them to you, Lord:
  may we always see this world as with your sight.

5 These our hands are yours, we give them to you, Lord:
  give them strength and skill to work and build for you.

6 These our tongues are yours, we give them to you, Lord:
  may we speak your healing words of light and truth.

7 These our feet are yours, we give them to you, Lord:
  may we always walk the path of light with you.

8 Our whole selves are yours, we give them to you, Lord:
  take us now and keep us safe for evermore.

66 I WILL SING UNTO THE LORD

NIGERIA

Words and music: unknown
arranged Geoff Weaver

With joy and rhythmic freedom ♩ = 112

I will sing un-to the Lord a joy-ful song, and bless his name for the Lord is good; I will sing un-to the Lord, I will sing un-to the Lord, I will

We heard this joyful song, rather reminiscent of Psalm 105 in its sentiments, sung with great verve and vitality by the Yorubas of Nigeria. Feel the rhythm rather than counting it, and don't be afraid to exercise freedom and creativity.

1.

sing un - to the Lord ev - ery day._____

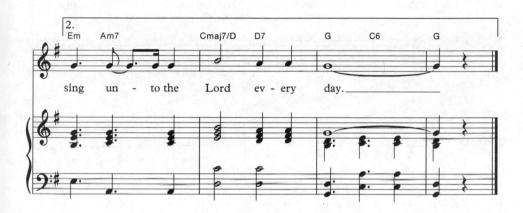

2.

sing un - to the Lord ev - ery day._____

I will sing unto the Lord a joyful song,
and bless his name for the Lord is good;
I will sing unto the Lord a joyful song,
and bless his name for the Lord is good.
    I will sing unto the Lord,
    I will sing unto the Lord,
    I will sing unto the Lord every day.
    I will sing unto the Lord,
    I will sing unto the Lord,
    I will sing unto the Lord every day.

67 ID Y PREDICAD
Go in Jesus' name

SPAIN

Words: from Luke 6, 9, 10 etc.
Josep La Porta, translated Word & Music
Music: Josep La Porta
arranged David Peacock

Steadily ♩ = 125

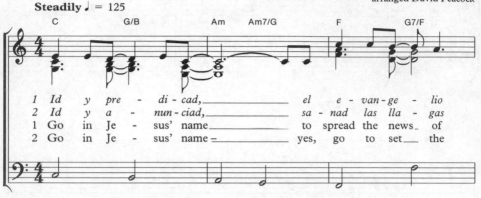

1 Id y pre - di - cad,_____ el e - van - ge - lio
2 Id y a - nun - ciad,_____ sa - nad las lla - gas
1 Go in Je - sus' name_____ to spread the news__ of
2 Go in Je - sus' name =_____ yes, go to set__ the

de la paz;__ al - zad los o - jos pa - ra ver__ que es
del do - lor,__ se - cad los o - jos, con - so - lad,__ que el
joy and peace: the har - vest fields are rea - dy now — it's
pris - oners free,__ to preach the good__ news to the poor, to

tiem - po de__ se - gar.__ Id y con - fi - ad,
mun - do llo - ran - do es - tá.__ Id y res - tau - rad,
time__ to start__ to reap.__ Go — his love__ pro - claim:
com - fort those who weep.__ Go to heal__ the lame,

A call to action from one of Spain's notable Christian musicians. A strong rhythmic character is essential, particularly in the syncopation of the refrain. However, the song should not be taken too fast.

que sus pro - me - sas cum - pli - rá;____ pa -
al que bran - ta - do co - ra - zón,____ su
his pro - mis - es____ will be ful - filled, and
bind up the wea - ry, bro - ken hearts; for

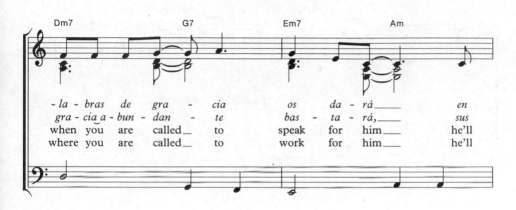

-la - bras de gra - cia os da - rá____ en
gra - cia_a - bun - dan - te bas - ta - rá,____ sus
when you are called_ to speak for him__ he'll
where you are called_ to work for him__ he'll

ca - da ne - ce - si - dad.____
car - gas a - li - via - rá.____
give you the words_ to say.____
give you his strength each day.____

Pa - ra que_el mun - do____ cre - a,____
Let all the world_ be - lieve him,__

pa - ra que el mun - do se - pa:___ que en él hay per - dón,___
let all the world re - ceive him!___ In Christ there is peace,

_____ que en él hay po - der,___
_____ in Christ there is power;___

pa - ra que el mun - do se - pa hoy.
Christ is the hope___ of all the world.

INSTRUMENTAL LINK AND ENDING

1 *Id y predicad,*
  el evangelio de la paz;
  alzad los ojos para ver
  que es tiempo de segar.
  Id y confiad
  que sus promesas cumplirá;
  palabras de gracia os dará
  en cada necesidad.

      Para que el mundo crea,
      para que el mundo sepa:
      que en él hay perdón,
      que en él hay poder,
      para que el mundo sepa hoy.

1 Go in Jesus' name
  to spread the news of joy and peace:
  the harvest fields are ready now –
  it's time to start to reap.
  Go – his love proclaim:
  his promises will be fulfilled,
  and when you are called to speak for him
  he'll give you the words to say.

      Let all the world believe him,
      let all the world receive him!
      In Christ there is peace,
      in Christ there is power;
      Christ is the hope of all the world.

2 *Id y anunciad,*
  sanad las llagas del dolor,
  secad los ojos, consolad,
  que el mundo llorando está.
  Id y restaurad,
  al que brantado corazón,
  su gracia abundante bastará,
  sus cargas aliviará.

      Para que . . .

2 Go in Jesus' name –
  yes, go to set the prisoners free,
  to preach the good news to the poor,
  to comfort those who weep.
  Go to heal the lame,
  bind up the weary, broken hearts;
  for where you are called to work for him
  he'll give you his strength each day.

      Let all the world . . .

68 IMELA
We thank you

NIGERIA

Words and music:
Christ Church Gospel Band, Umani-Enugu
arranged Iona Community

Brightly ♩ = 88

I - me - la, i - me - la, i - me - la, O - ka - ka.
We thank you, thank you Lord, we thank you, our great God.

I - me - la, Chi - ne - ke. I - me - le On - y'o - ma.
We thank you, gra-cious Lord, we thank you, our great God.

Imela, imela, imela, Okaka.
Imela, Chineke. Imele Ony'oma.

We thank you, thank you Lord,
we thank you, our great God.
We thank you, gracious Lord,
we thank you, our great God.

An Igbo song of thanksgiving, popular all over Nigeria. It requires freedom of expression, movement, handclaps, drumbeats and many repetitions to capture the authentic Nigerian flavour.

Words and music: © 1990 Christ Church Gospel Band, Box 4234
Umani-Enugu, Anambra State, Nigeria,
as taught by Mrs Unoaku Ekwegbalu

69 ISA MASIH
Jesus the Lord is seeking me

PAKISTAN

Words: translated from the original
by Alison Blenkinsop
Music: unknown

Unhurried ♩. = 48

I - sa ma-sih ma la - ta - vi ma da gu-nah na tcha

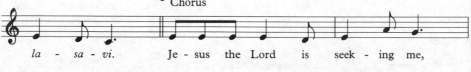

Chorus

la - sa - vi. Je - sus the Lord is seek - ing me,

Fine Verse

and from my sin he will set me free.
1 Who is the one who
2 Why does he care so
3 This is the rea - son –

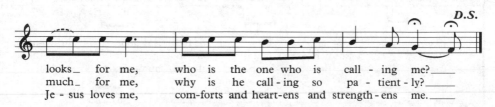

D.S.

looks_ for me, who is the one who is call - ing me?___
much_ for me, why is he call-ing so pa - tient - ly?___
Je - sus loves me, com-forts and heart-ens and strength-ens me.___

4 How can he give such comfort to me –
   there is such weakness and sin in me.
     Jesus the Lord ...

5 He gave his life in sacrifice
   and for my sin he has paid the price.
     Jesus the Lord ...

6 I am so glad he set me free –
   I'll live with God for eternity.
     Jesus the Lord ...

> This haunting song comes from the North-West Frontier province of Pakistan, and is best sung unaccompanied. Christians in Pakistan are in a small minority. It is good that we remember them and identify with them as we sing this song.

SPAIN

Esta noche

Words: Michael Perry
Music: Spanish carol melody
arranged Tom Cunningham

This lovely Spanish carol requires both rhythmic vitality and a certain gentleness in performance. It is very effective if the chorus is sung in harmony.

Chorus

bring you.
- lov - èd.
ly - ing.

There's a light in the hea - vens this

morn-ing and a song for the an - gels to sing; in a

sta-ble,__ in a man-ger, lies a ba - by =__ our true sav-iour.

sav-iour.

Instrumental ending

PAKISTAN

Words: from Psalm 62
translated from the Punjabi
by Alison Blenkinsop
Music: unknown
arranged Geoff Weaver

Confidently ♩. = 68

Chorus

In si-lent still-ness, wait for God and rest, my soul, in peace:____ in

last time **to Coda** ⊕

him your hopes will be ful-filled, your fears will find re-

Verse

- lease.____ 1 He is the for-tress of my soul, he is the for-tress
2 He is my strong de-liv-er-er, he is my strong de-
3 Let all the na-tions trust in him, let all the na-tions

This expressive Punjabi setting of words from Psalm 62 is sung by Pakistani Christians who are a very small minority in an Islamic state. Although in the minor key, it should be sung with rhythm and conviction. When changing from ⁶/₈ to ⁹/₈, the speed of the dotted crotchet is equal to the crotchet of the new pattern.

of my soul — my Rock, my hid - ing - place, _____ my
-liv - er - er - I'm safe with-in ___ his hand, _____ I'm
trust in him and bow be - fore ___ his throne, _____ and

Rock, my hid - ing - place; ___ so I shall not be o - ver-come, de -
safe with-in ___ his hand, ___ the Lord is my de-fend-er and the
bow be-fore ___ his throne, ___ and wor-ship him with hum-ble hearts — for

-feat I'll ne - ver face, so I shall not be o - ver-come, de -
rock on which I stand, the Lord is my de-fend-er and the
he is God a - lone, and wor-ship him with hum-ble hearts — for

⊕ CODA

-feat I'll ne-ver face!
rock on which I stand. In
he is God a-lone.

fears will find re-lease.

KYRIE

Words: traditional
Music: unknown
arranged Geoff Weaver

A solo-response Kyrie eleison (Lord, have mercy), characteristically Indian in its melodic shape. It should be sung with heartfelt yearning.

73 JE LOUERAI L'ÉTERNEL
I long to praise the Lord

FRANCE

Words: from Psalm 9, L. Sogond
translated Robert Atkins
Music: unknown
arranged Geoff Weaver

Worshipfully ♩ = 88
VERSION 1

1 Je   loue-rai l'É - ter - nel   de   tout   mon___
1 I   long to praise the Lord   with   all   of   my

cœur,   je   ra - con - te - rai   tou - tes   tes mer-veil - les, je
heart,   in   praise   to be sung   by each   tribe and tongue_   I

chan - te - rai ton   nom.___   Je   loue-rai l'É - ter - nel   de
long   to sing my   part.___   I   long to praise the Lord   with

tout   mon___   cœur,   je   fe - rai de toi   le
all   of my   heart,   I   long   to em-ploy   my

> A gentle song of worship from France. The two arrangements
> allow for either congregational or choral use.

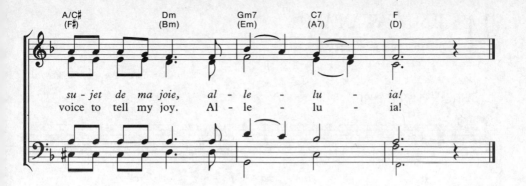

su - jet de ma joie, al - le - lu - ia!
voice to tell my joy. Al - le - lu - ia!

2 Dieu, l'Éternel est roi, il règne à jamais.
   Pour le jugement, il dresse son trône:
   il jugera la terre,
   Dieu, l'Éternel est roi, il règne à jamais.
   Le monde verra la force de son bras,
      alleluia!

3 Dieu voit les opprimés, il est leur abri,
   leur refuge au temps des grandes détresses.
   Son nom est leur salut.
   Dieu voit les opprimés, il est leur abri,
   il sauve les siens, car il est le Dieu Saint,
      alleluia!

4 Gloire au Père et au Fils et au Saint-Esprit
   au commencement, aujourd'hui, toujours
   et aux siècles des siècles.
   Gloire au Père et au Fils et au Saint-Esprit
   d'une éternité à l'autre éternité,
      alleluia!

2 No limits to the power of his mighty hand!
   We'll come to his throne, his justice to be known –
   for all to understand.
   No limits to the power of his mighty hand –
   creation will see how just and true is he.
      Alleluia!

3 With justice he is kind – he knows we are weak.
   His children in pain will rise up again –
   he loves to help the meek.
   With justice he is kind – he knows we are weak;
   the God we adore is faithful to the poor.
      Alleluia!

4 Sing out your praise to God the Three-in-One –
   we'll sing of the Lord, the Spirit, the Word,
   till earthly time is done.
   Sing out your praise to God the Three-in-One –
   we'll meet and adore when time shall be no more.
      Alleluia!

74 JESU TAWA PANO
Jesus, we are here

ZIMBABWE

Words and music: Patrick Matsikenyiri

With expression ♩ = 100

Je - su ta - wa pa - no; Je - su
Je - sus, we are here;__ Je - sus,

ta - wa pa - no; Je - su ta - wa pa - no;
we are here;__ Je - sus, we are here;__

(except last time)
Mam - bo Je - su.

ta - wa pa - no mu zi - ta re - nyu.
we are here_____ for_____ you.

A gathering song, originally from Shona, and composed by Patrick Matsikenyiri, a primary school headmaster and a leading composer of African Church music. The harmonic clash in bar five is deliberate. Patrick said to John Bell of the Iona Community, 'If you knew the history of our country, you would know that we have had so many clashes that a little difficulty in the harmony will cause us no problem.' Other verses may be added e.g. We are here *with* you, . . . *in* you.

75 JESUS CHRIST OUR LIVING LORD

HUNGARY

Words: after E. Turmezei
translated by E. Abraham and John L. Bell
Music: Szokolay Sandor
arranged Geoff Weaver

Steadily ♩ = 76

1 Je-sus Christ, our liv-ing Lord, we be-lieve you
2 In the humbl-est things we do we'll ac-count our -
3 Food e-nough that all may feed, grace e-nough for
4 Lord in all we do to-day let our lives pre-

keep your word: what-ev-er may be-fall us,
-selves to you; mak-ing your love our mea-sure,
each one's need even as we praise you, sing-ing
-pare your way; may peace and love be-friend us

stretch or stall us, we'll trust your voice to call us.
truth and trea-sure, your will our joy and plea-sure.
you come bring-ing gifts at the day's be-gin-ning.
and de-fend us wher-ev-er you may send us.

> Folk-song like in character, this hymn was published in a new hymnbook
> produced in 1981 by the Hungarian Ecumenical Council of Churches.

76 JESU, JESU, FILL US WITH YOUR LOVE

GHANA

Words: Tom Colvin
Music: Ghanaian melody
arranged Geoff Weaver

With a gentle lilt ♩. = 63

Je - su,_____ Je - su,_____ fill us with your love; show

Je - su, Je - su

us how to serve the neigh-bours we have from you.

Fine

UNISON

1 Kneels at the feet of his friends, si - lent - ly wash - es their
2 Neigh-bours are rich folk and poor; neigh-bours are black, brown and
3 These are the ones we should serve, these are the ones we should
4 Lov - ing puts us on our knees, serv - ing as though we were

One of the many hymns from Ghana originally collected by Tom Colvin. This 'song of service' has been included in many modern hymn books in recent years.
Suggested drum pattern:

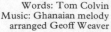

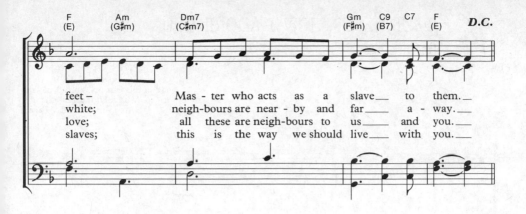

Jesu, Jesu, fill us with your love;
show us how to serve the neighbours we have from you.

1 Kneels at the feet of his friends,
silently washes their feet –
Master who acts as a slave to them.
    Jesu, Jesu . . .

2 Neighbours are rich folk and poor;
neighbours are black, brown and white;
neighbours are nearby and far away.
    Jesu, Jesu . . .

3 These are the ones we should serve,
these are the ones we should love;
all these are neighbours to us and you.
    Jesu, Jesu . . .

4 Loving puts us on our knees,
serving as though we were slaves;
this is the way we should live with you.
    Jesu, Jesu . . .

77 JESUS, JESUS, HOW I ADORE YOU
Jai, Jai, Yisu

Words: after C. D. Rockley
and in this version Word & Music
Music: Hindustani melody
arranged Geoff Weaver

Je - sus, Je - sus, how I a - dore___ you,

Chorus

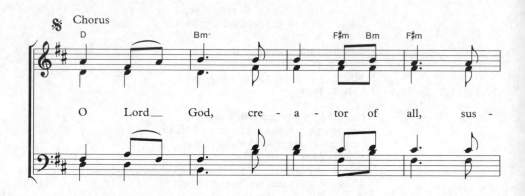

O Lord___ God, cre - a - tor of all, sus -

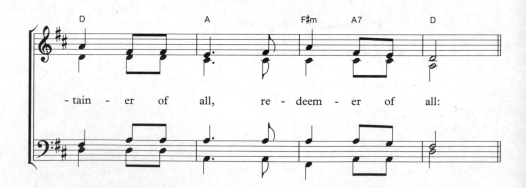

-tain - er of all, re - deem - er of all:

> An earthy rhythmical refrain which is based on an Hindustani folk melody, and has something of the character of a folk dance. The verse should be more delicate in style.

Fine

Je - sus, Je - sus, how I a - dore___ you!

SOLO

1 Leav - ing your glo - ry, with love your great de - sign,___
2 When I___ come to___ you___ in my pain___
3 Al - le - lu - ia;___ glo - ry,___ glo - ry!___

giv - ing your life, and___ so re - deem - ing mine;___
you give___ me your___ peace___ once a - gain;___
Ev - ery - bo - dy, tell___ the___ sto - ry.

1st time SOLO
2nd time ALL (HARMONY)

D.S. al Fine

O Lord Je - sus, come; O Joy - giv - er come;
Re - liev - ing___ my load, guid - ing my road;
Come one, come___ all, come heed God's___ call;

78 JESUS THE LORD SAID

Words: anonymous
translated Dermott Monahan
Music: Urdu melody
arranged Geoff Weaver

1 Je - sus the Lord said: 'I am the Bread, the Bread of___ Life for the
2 Je - sus the Lord said: 'I am the Door, the Way and the Door for the
3 Je - sus the Lord said: 'I am the Light, the one true_ Light of the

world am I. The Bread of___ Life for the world am I, the
poor am I. The Way and the Door for the poor am I, the
world am I. The one true_ Light of the world am I, the

Bread of___ Life for the world am I.' Je - sus the Lord said:
Way and the Door for the poor am I.' Je - sus the Lord said:
one true_ Light of the world am I.' Je - sus the Lord said:

> One of the most widely travelled of Indian hymns, this haunting melody
> is Urdu in origin. It makes an ideal vehicle through which to teach many
> of Jesus' sayings about himself, and may be expanded ad lib.

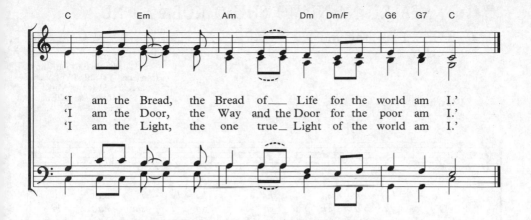

'I am the Bread, the Bread of___ Life for the world am I.'
'I am the Door, the Way and the Door for the poor am I.'
'I am the Light, the one true_ Light of the world am I.'

1 Jesus the Lord said: 'I am the Bread,
the Bread of Life for the world am I.
   The Bread of Life for the world am I,
   the Bread of Life for the world am I.'
Jesus the Lord said: 'I am the Bread,
the Bread of Life for the world am I.'

2 Jesus the Lord said: 'I am the Door,
the Way and the Door for the poor am I . . .'

3 Jesus the Lord said: 'I am the Light,
the one true Light of the world am I . . .'

4 Jesus the Lord said: 'I am the Shepherd,
the one Good Shepherd of the sheep am I . . .'

5 Jesus the Lord said: 'I am the Life,
the Resurrection and the Life am I . . .'

79

KATA KU NA NI MO SHU O KOBA MI NU
Here I am, the one

JAPAN

Words: Yukiko Ishiyama
translated Yasuhiko Yokosaka
paraphrased James Minchin
Music: Akira Tanaka
arranged Geoff Weaver

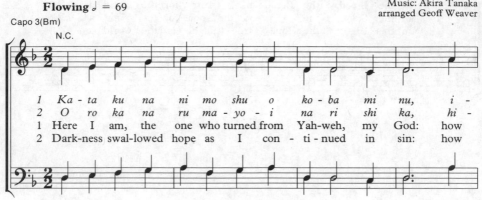

1 Ka - ta ku na ni mo shu o ko - ba mi nu, i-
2 O ro ka na ru ma - yo - i na ri shi ka, hi-
1 Here I am, the one who turned from Yah-weh, my God: how
2 Dark-ness swal-lowed hope as I con - ti - nued in sin: how

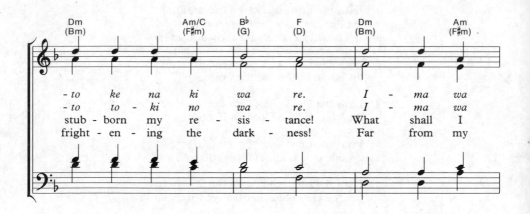

- to ke na ki wa re. I - ma wa
- to to - ki no wa re. I - ma wa
stub - born my re - sis - tance! What shall I
fright - en - ing the dark - ness! Far from my

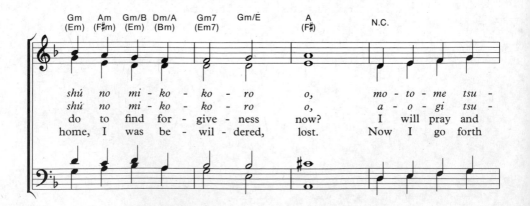

shú no mi - ko - ko - ro o, mo - to - me tsu-
shú no mi - ko - ko - ro o, a - o - gi tsu-
do to find for - give - ness now? I will pray and
home, I was be - wil - dered, lost. Now I go forth

There is an austere joy in this song of repentance and new life, perhaps reflecting the often turbulent history of the small Christian community in Japan.

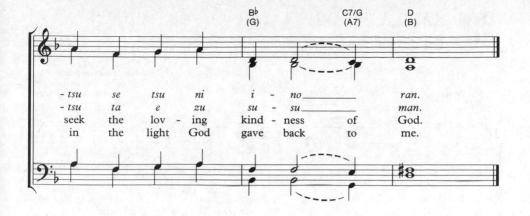

				Bb (G)			C7/G (A7)	D (B)

-tsu se tsu ni i -no_____ ran.
-tsu ta e zu su -su_____ man.
seek the lov-ing kind-ness of God.
in the light God gave back to me.

1 *Kata ku na ni mo shu o koba mi nu,*
ito ke na ki wa re.
Ima wa shú no mikokoro o,
motome tsutsu se tsu ni ino ran.

2 *O ro ka na ru mayoi na ri shi ka,*
hito toki no wa re.
Ima wa shú no mikokoro o,
aogi tsutsu ta e zu susu man.

3 *No ni yama ni hikari ahure te,*
suku wa re shi wa re.
Ima wa shú no mimegumi o,
Taka raka ni tatae uta wan.

1 Here I am, the one who turned from Yahweh, my God:
how stubborn my resistance!
What shall I do to find forgiveness now?
I will pray and seek the loving kindness of God.

2 Darkness swallowed hope as I continued in sin:
how frightening the darkness!
Far from my home, I was bewildered, lost.
Now I go forth in the light God gave back to me.

3 All around, the landscape shines with new light and life,
the fields and mountains glisten!
Jesus' salvation fills the world with joy.
I will praise and sing God's goodness while I have breath.

80 KATIKA SAFARI
On the journey to heaven

KENYA

Words and music: unknown
English: Word & Music
arranged Geoff Weaver

March-like ♩ = 112

1 Ka - ti - ka sa - fa - ri ya kwen - da m(bin)-gu - ni
2 U - ki - wa u - si - ku u - ki - wa mch - an - a
3 U - ki - fi - ka ku - le, u - ta - pum zi - ka

1 On the jour - ney to hea - ven we'll walk with the Lord,
2 On the jour - ney to hea - ven we'll live in the light,
3 On the jour - ney to hea - ven he'll give us his rest,

Tem - be - a na Bwa - na Ye - su, Ka - ti -
Tem - be - a na Bwa - na Ye - su, U - ki -
Tem - be - a na Bwa - na Ye - su, U - ki -

he will walk with us on our way; when we
he will shine light up - on our way; when we
he will give rest up - on our way; when he

- ka sa - fa - ri ya kwen - da m(bin)-gu - ni
- wa u - si - ku u - ki - wa mch - an - a
- fi - ka ku - le, u - ta - pum zi - ka

walk with the Lord he will lead by his word —
live in the light we shall not fear the night —
gives us his rest, we'll know his way is best —

The Christian life is often portrayed as a journey, following the Way, and this
East African song has a typical exuberance and rhythmic vitality, depicting the
march of the pilgrims. Add descants and drums ad lib.

81

KAY YAHWEH AKO
I'll follow my Lord

PHILIPPINES

Words: from the Tagalog
in this version Word & Music
Music: unknown
arranged Geoff Weaver

Relaxed, easy flow ♩ = 88

Kay Yah-weh a-ko, kay Yah-weh a-ko Kay
I'll fol-low my Lord, I'll fol-low my Lord, I'll

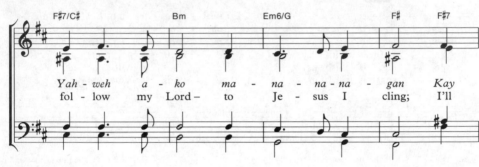

Yah-weh a-ko ma-na-na-na-gan Kay
fol-low my Lord— to Je-sus I cling; I'll

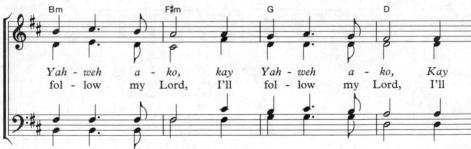

Yah-weh a-ko, kay Yah-weh a-ko, Kay
fol-low my Lord, I'll fol-low my Lord, I'll

Yah-weh a-ko ma-na-na-gan.
fol-low my Lord— my love I will bring!

The arranger heard this beautiful song sung by Filipino Christians who had
recently suffered devastation from earthquake, volcanic eruption and typhoon.
In that context, to sing, 'to Jesus I cling', has tremendous power and rel-
evance. Its folk-song character is well served by a guitar accompaniment.

82 KHUDAYA, RAHEM KAR

Have mercy on us, Lord

PAKISTAN

Words: traditional
Music: traditional Urdu
arranged Geoff Weaver

KYRIE

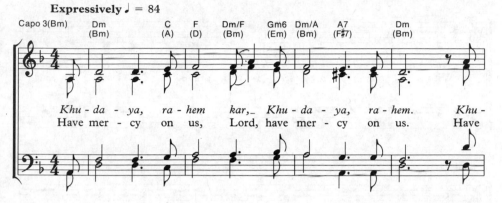

Khu-da-ya, ra-hem kar,_ Khu-da-ya, ra-hem. Khu-
Have mer-cy on us, Lord, have mer-cy on us. Have

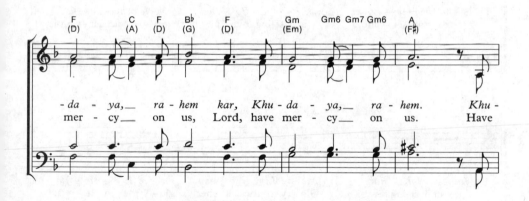

-da-ya,_ ra-hem kar, Khu-da-ya,_ ra-hem. Khu-
mer-cy_ on us, Lord, have mer-cy_ on us. Have

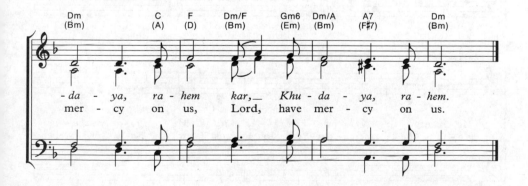

-da-ya, ra-hem kar,_ Khu-da-ya, ra-hem.
mer-cy on us, Lord, have mer-cy on us.

> This expressive Kyrie was sung at the W.C.C. Seventh Assembly in Canberra in
> 1991. The Indian subcontinent is often devastated by natural disasters and this
> plea for mercy may be sung both in a personal and a corporate sense.

83 KHUSHI KUSHI MANAO
With a song in my heart

INDIA

Words and music: unknown
English: Word & Music
music arranged Geoff Weaver

Gently ♩ = 108

Khu-shi ku-shi man-ao, Khu-shi ku-shi man-ao Bo-lo
With a song in my heart I will praise you, O Lord, for your

bo-lo ma-shi-ha-ki Jai, Jai, Jai Bo-lo bo-lo ma-shi-ha-ki
gift to your ser-vant is ev-er-last-ing love, for your gift to your ser-vant is

Fine

Jai, Jai, Jai. Me-re Liy-a aya, me-re Liy-a Jia
ev-er-last-ing love. Glo-ry to the Fa-ther, glo-ry be to Je-sus,

Me-re Liy-a aya, me-re Liy-a Jia. Me-re Liy-a ye-shu-ne
glo-ry to the Fa-ther, glo-ry be to Je-sus, to the Ho-ly Spi-rit be

There is a quiet joy about this Indian song, first sung to the arranger by an Indian pastor's wife who shared fully and sacrificially in her husband's demanding rural ministry. The repetition in the phrases allows for a leader-congregation format, but it should never be boisterous.

C/G　G7　C　　　Em　　　　　F　　　　　C/G　G7　C

duth＿ u - tha-ya　　Me - re Liy - a　ye-shu - ne　duth＿ u - tha-ya.
glo - ry ev - er-more,　to　the Ho - ly Spi-rit　be　glo - ry ev - er-more;

F　　　　　　　　　　　　　　C

Me - re Liy - a　Ma - ra　ga-ya,　me - re Liy - a,　ga - ra　ga - ya
glo - ry in the high-est hea-ven,　to　our God be glo - ry gi - ven,

F　　　　　　　　　　　　　　C

Me - re Liy - a　Ma - ra　ga-ya,　me - re Liy - a,　ga - ra　ga - ya.
glo - ry in the high-est hea-ven,　to　our God be glo - ry gi - ven

C/E　　　　　F　　　　　C/G　　　G7　　　C

Me - re Liy - a　fia - ji　u - tha,　me - re hai ma - sih
for　his faith-ful-ness to-wards us　and　his sav - ing grace,

D.S. al Fine

Am　　　　　　　　　　Fmaj7

Mai　ma-shi - ka hun,　　ham　ma-shi - ka hai. Khu - shi
and　his sav - ing grace,　　and　his sav - ing grace. With a

84 KOSKETA MINUA, HENKI
Touch me, God's Spirit

FINLAND

Words: Anna-Maija Raittila
English: Matti Kilpio
Music: Ilkka Kuusisto
arranged Geoff Weaver

Flowing ♩ = 144

1 Kos - ke - ta mi - nu - a, Hen - ki! Kos - ke - ta,
2 Kos - ke - ta, Ju - ma - lan Hen - ki, sy - väl - le
1 Touch me, God's Spi - rit e - ter - nal, touch me, res -
2 Touch me, God's Spi - rit, and soothe me deep in my

kirk - ka - us! An - na e - lä
sy - däme - en. Sin - ne pa - ina
-plen - dent Light; give my life new
rest - less soul; give me trust in

- mäl - le suun - ta ja tar - koi - tus.
hil - jaa luot - ta - mus Je - esuk - seen.
mean - ing, show me the true and right.
Je - sus, heal me and make me whole.

A gentle song of invitation to the Holy Spirit from the Christian community in Finland.

1 *Kosketa minua, Henki!*
  Kosketa, kirkkaus!
  Anna elämälle
  suunta ja tarkoitus.

2 *Kosketa, Jumalan Henki,*
  syvälle sydämeen.
  Sinne paina hiljaa
  luottamus Jeesukseen.

3 *Rohkaise minua, Henki,*
  murenna pelkoni.
  Tässä maailmassa
  osoita paikkani.

4 *Valaise, Jumalan Henki,*
  silmäni aukaise,
  että voisin olla
  ystävä toisille.

5 *Kosketa minua, Henki!*
  Herätä kiittämään,
  sinun lähelläsi
  armosta elämään.

1 Touch me, God's Spirit eternal,
  touch me, resplendent Light;
  give my life new meaning,
  show me the true and right.

2 Touch me, God's Spirit, and soothe me
  deep in my restless soul;
  give me trust in Jesus,
  heal me and make me whole.

3 Spirit of God, give me courage,
  banish my doubts and fears;
  show me my vocation
  through all my days and years.

4 Spirit of God, brightly shining,
  open my eyes to see
  those who need my friendship –
  join us in unity.

5 Touch me, God's Spirit eternal,
  teach me to thank and praise;
  by your grace be near me,
  guide me in all my ways.

85 KUNIN MO ANG AKING PUSO
Let me tell you how I need you

PHILIPPINES

Words and music: Teresita Valeriano
English: Word & Music
music arranged Geoff Weaver

With intensity ♩ = 72

1 Ku - nin Mo ang a - king pu - so;
2 Ku - nin Mo ang a - king bu - hay;
1 Let me tell you how I need you;
2 In your mer - cy, Lord, for - give me,

ku - sang i - bi - ni - bi - gay i - to. He -
sa 'Yo a - king i - na - a - lay. He -
take my love, I give it to____ you: for
by your grace come, cleanse, re - new____ me: for

- sus ang 'Yong pag - ma - ma - hal ang ma -
- sus sa 'Yong ka - la - ka - san ay na -
you have died to____ bring me life – O Lord
you a - lone can____ change my life – O Lord

A rich and passionate 'prayer in song', composed by a former student at the Asian School for
Music, Worship and the Arts in Manila, and firmly rooted in her vibrant Filipino culture.
Allow the alternation between four and three beats in a bar to flow naturally.

Ebm7
(Dm7)

Cm9
(Bm7)

F7
(E7)

- na - na - han   sa   pu - song   pa -   gal.
- is   ki - tang   ma - pag - ling - ku - ran.
Je - sus Christ, you're my heart's   de -   sire!
Je - sus Christ, you're the   liv - ing   fire.

Bbm
(Am)

Ebm
(Dm)

F7
(E7)

Da - hil   I - kaw ang bu - hay   at   ang   ka - to - to -
Je - sus,   I want to know you,   Je - sus,   I want to

Bbm
(Am)

Ebm7
(Dm7)

- ha -   nan,   a -   king   i - si - nu -
serve   you;   Je - sus,   I   want   to

Db/F
(C)

F7
(E7)

Bbm
(Am)

- su -   ko   bu - hay   na   mu - la   sa - 'Yo.
love   you –   love you more,   to love you more.

86 KYRIE ELEISON
Lord, have mercy

RUSSIA

Words: traditional
Music: Russian Orthodox

KYRIE

Ky - ri - e e - lei - son. Ky - ri - e e - lei - son.
Lord,_____ have mer - cy. Lord,_____ have mer - cy.

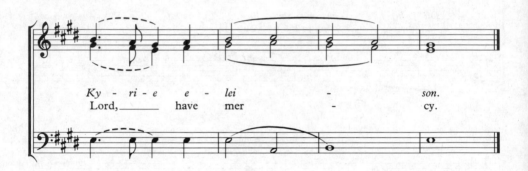

Ky - ri - e e - lei - son.
Lord,_____ have mer - cy.

Kyrie eleison.
Kyrie eleison.
Kyrie eleison.

Lord, have mercy.
Lord, have mercy.
Lord, have mercy.

Originally from the Russian Orthodox Church, this simple chant is ideal for encouraging a congregation to sing in harmony. It may be used repeatedly as a focus for meditation.

87 KYRIE ELEISON
Lord, have mercy

GHANA

Words: traditional
Music: Dinah Reindorf
arranged Geoff Weaver

It is not too fanciful to hear in this expressive Kyrie, with echoes of the blues in its final phrase, so much of the pain and suffering of Ghana's colonial past with its slave trade and enforced break-up of families. Dinah Reindorf, one of Ghana's leading musicians, composed this in response to a Passion Walk, walking in Christ's footsteps to the cross.

88 LA ALEGRÍA ESTÁ EN EL CORAZÓN

Joy, wonderful and free

ARGENTINA

Words: unknown
English: Word & Music
Music: unknown
arranged David Peacock

Lively ♩ = 130

La a-le-grí-a es - tá en el co - ra-zón___ de a-
Joy, won-der-ful and free fills our hearts to-day:___ so

-quel que co - no - ce a Je - sús.
come, praise the name of our sav - iour!___

La ver-da-de - ra___ paz la tie - ne a-quel___ que
Live in the Spi - rit,___ walk in hea - ven's way,___ and

ya co - no - ce a Je - sús;___
give your love to our sav - iour.___

A popular song throughout Central America which relies on
a strong and steady rhythmic accompaniment.

La alegría está en el corazón
de aquel que conoce a Jesús.
La verdadera paz la tiene
aquel que ya conoce a Jesús;
¡oh! sentimiento más precioso que viene del Señor,
el amor de aquel que ya conoce a Jesús.

Joy, wonderful and free
    fills our hearts today:
so come, praise the name of our saviour!
Live in the Spirit,
    walk in heaven's way,
and give your love to our saviour.
Peace from the Father
    comes when we pray,
and all our burdens he bears.
Let us bow down in worship
    and exalt Jesus' name!

89 LA VENIDA DE CRISTO
When the stars in their flight

CHILE

Words: Santiago Stevenson
English: From Mark 13, Michael Perry
Music: Chilean melody
arranged Geoff Weaver

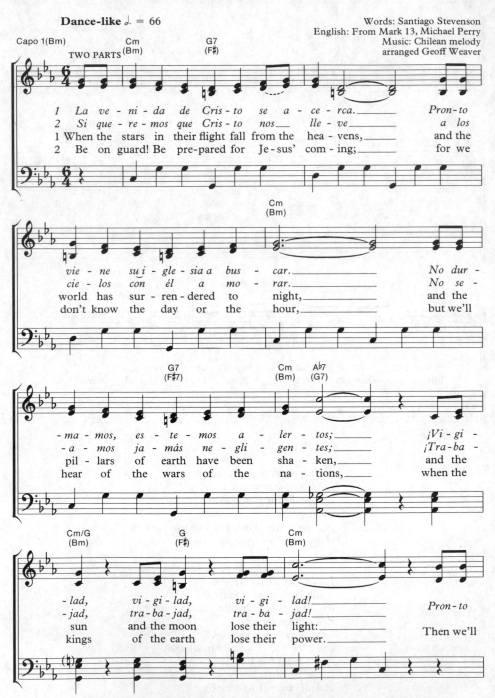

1 La ve-ni-da de Cris-to se a-ce-rca._____ Pron-to
2 Si que-re-mos que Cris-to nos__ lle-ve_____ a los
1 When the stars in their flight fall from the hea-vens,_____ and the
2 Be on guard! Be pre-pared for Je-sus' com-ing;_____ for we

vie-ne su i-gle-sia a bus-car._____ No dur-
cie-los con él a mo-rar._____ No se-
world has sur-ren-dered to night,_____ and the
don't know the day or the hour,_____ but we'll

-ma-mos, es-te-mos a-ler-tos;_____ ¡Vi-gi-
-a-mos ja-más ne-gli-gen-tes;_____ ¡Tra-ba-
pil-lars of earth have been sha-ken,_____ and the
hear of the wars of the na-tions,_____ when the

-lad, vi-gi-lad, vi-gi-lad!_____ Pron-to
-jad, tra-ba-jad, tra-ba-jad!_____ Then we'll
sun and the moon lose their light:_____
kings of the earth lose their power._____

There has been astonishing growth in the Protestant churches in Latin America in recent years. New Christians are encouraged to sing songs which grow from their own culture, and this lively dance song is a good example of such 'enculturation'. Add percussion instruments and guitars as you wish.

3 Arreglemos, estemos a cuentas
con Jesús, el Cordero de Dios.
Del que ofende tengamos clemencia;
¡Perdonad, perdonad, perdonad!
  Pronto viene . . .

4 Perdonando, Jesús nos perdona,
y nos lleva con él a reinar.
Ganaremos también la corona;
¡Vigilad, trabajad, perdonad!
  Pronto viene . . .

3 We can trust in the presence of the Spirit,
he will teach us what we are to say;
and we need not be fearful or anxious,
for his grace will provide in that day.
  Then we'll see the Lord . . .

4 When the leaves of the fig tree are emerging,
then we see that the summer is near,
even so, as these things start to happen
then you know that the Son will appear.
  Then we'll see the Lord . . .

90 LAUDATE DOMINUM
Sing praise and bless the Lord

FRANCE

Words: from Psalm 117
Music: Jacques Berthier
Taizé Community

Joyfully ♩ = 116

OSTINATO − MIXED VOICES

EQUAL VOICES

A powerful Taizé chant suitable for times of praise and celebration.

91 LET MY SPIRIT REJOICE IN YOUR LOVE

PAKISTAN

Words: from the Urdu
Alison Blenkinsop
Music: unknown
arranged Geoff Weaver

Lilting ♩ = 112

Capo 3(Am)

Chorus

Let my spi - rit re - joice in your love, O my Lord – I will
healed by your love shown on Cal - va - ry___ of my
o - pened the door, let your bright - ness_ in___ now my
all at your feet, let me wor - ship_ you – my de -
giv - en me joy that the world can - not give, joy that

tell of your won - der - ful grace; you have
guilt there is left not a trace; all is
world is a beau - ti - ful place; you have
- sire is to look on your face; cast - ing
no - thing can ev - er ef - face; you have

brought me to life through your liv - ing Word, I am
healed by your love shown on Cal - va - ry___ of my
o - pened the door, let your bright - ness in___ now my
all at your feet, let me wor - ship you – my de -
given me joy that the world can - not give,_ joy that

An Urdu song which somehow combines a minor mode and an expression of real joy.
It should move quite quickly. The chorus may be sung by all, while the verse should be solo.

LET US GREET ONE ANOTHER

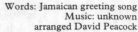

JAMAICA

Words: Jamaican greeting song
Music: unknown
arranged David Peacock

It is difficult to feel excluded when worshipping in the Caribbean.
This song would be ideal for the exchange of greetings or the Peace.

93 LOE DE ÍSÁ
Jesus knows the inmost heart

PAKISTAN

Words: from the Pushto, Alison Blenkinsop
Music: unknown
arranged Geoff Weaver

Flowing ♩ = 60

Chorus HARMONY

repeat first time only **Fine**

Lo - e de Í - sá ust - áz hál - da zra tá go - rí.
Je - sus knows the in - most heart – no - thing can be hid - den.

Verse UNISON

1 This our sin - ful hearts re - quire, flame of God's re - fin - ing fire
2 Je - sus knows our deep - est fears, knows the pain of hid - den tears;
3 When our lives are in his hand no - thing can his work with - stand;
4 So our faith will be re - stored by the word of Christ our Lord;

D.C.

work - ing in us day by day till the dross is burned a - way.
by his words of love and peace ev - ery heart can find_ re - lease.
his for - give - ness sets us free, saves us for e - ter - ni - ty.
for the warmth his love im - parts melts the ve - ry hard - est hearts.

One of a number of songs from the Pushto-speaking Christians of Pakistan which have been collected by Alison Blenkinsop (formerly Fookes), who served as a missionary there. Both melody and text have a simplicity and directness which is very appealing.

94 LET US TALENTS AND TONGUES EMPLOY

JAMAICA

Words: Fred Kaan
Music: Jamaican folk song
arranged David Peacock

Freely and joyfully ♩ = 152

1 Let us tal - ents and tongues em - ploy,
2 Christ is a - ble to make us one,_
3 Je - sus calls_ us in, sends us out_

reach - ing out with a shout of joy:_ bread is bro - ken, the
at his ta - ble he set the tone, teach - ing peo - ple to
bear - ing fruit_ in a world of doubt, gives us love_ to tell,

wine is poured, Christ is spo - ken and seen and heard.
live, to bless, love in word and in deed ex - press.
bread to share: God Em - ma - nu - el ev - ery - where!

This 'sending out' song is one of the many fruits of the collaboration in
Geneva between the Jamaican Doreen Potter and the hymn writer Fred Kaan.
Based on a Jamaican folk song, it must always be vitally rhythmic.

Je - sus lives__ a - gain, earth can breathe a - gain,

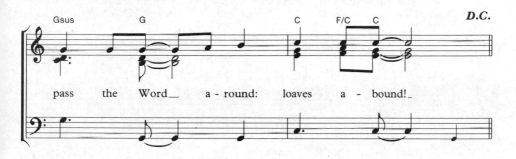

pass the Word__ a - round: loaves a - bound!_

1 Let us talents and tongues employ,
   reaching out with a shout of joy:
   bread is broken, the wine is poured,
   Christ is spoken and seen and heard.
      Jesus lives again,
      earth can breathe again,
      pass the Word around:
      loaves abound!

2 Christ is able to make us one,
   at his table he set the tone,
   teaching people to live, to bless,
   love in word and in deed express.
      Jesus lives again . . .

3 Jesus calls us in, sends us out
   bearing fruit in a world of doubt,
   gives us love to tell, bread to share:
   God Emmanuel everywhere!
      Jesus lives again . . .

95 LOOK AND LEARN

KOREA

Words: from Matthew 6: 23–34
John L. Bell
Music: Nah Young-Soo
arranged Geoff Weaver

Flowing ♩· = 56

1 Look and learn from the birds of the air, fly - ing high a-bove
2 Look and learn from the flowers of the field, bring - ing beau - ty and
3 What God wants_ should be_ our will; where God calls_ should

wor - ry and fear; nei - ther sow - ing nor har - vest-ing seed,
col - our to life; nei - ther sew - ing nor tail - or - ing cloth,
be_ our goal. When we seek_ the King - dom first,

yet they're gi - ven what - ev - er they need. If the God of
yet they're dressed in the fin - est at - tire. If the God of
all we've lost_ is ours_ a - gain. Let's be done with

> On hearing this haunting pentatonic melody, many people are surprised to learn
> of its Korean origin. This should have an easy flow, not moving too slowly.

earth and heaven cares for birds as much__ as this,
earth and heaven cares for flowers as much__ as this,
anx - ious thoughts, set a - side to - mor - row's cares,

won't he care much more for you, if you put_ your trust_ in him?
won't he care much more for you if you put_ your trust_ in him?
live each day_ that God pro-vides put-ting all__ our trust_ in him.

1 Look and learn from the birds of the air,
flying high above worry and fear;
neither sowing nor harvesting seed,
yet they're given whatever they need.
If the God of earth and heaven
cares for birds as much as this,
won't he care much more for you,
if you put your trust in him?

2 Look and learn from the flowers of the field,
bringing beauty and colour to life;
neither sewing nor tailoring cloth,
yet they're dressed in the finest attire.
If the God of earth and heaven
cares for flowers as much as this,
won't he care much more for you
if you put your trust in him?

3 What God wants should be our will;
where God calls should be our goal.
When we seek the Kingdom first,
all we've lost is ours again.
Let's be done with anxious thoughts,
set aside tomorrow's cares,
live each day that God provides
putting all our trust in him.

LORD, FORGIVE ME

CHINA

Words: Ellsworth Candlee
Music: Confucian Chant
arranged Geoff Weaver

♩ = 92

1 Lord, for - give___ me. Christ, have mer - cy!
2 Lord, for - give___ me. Christ, have mer - cy!

ORGAN PEDAL

I con - fess to you all my sin and shame.
Now to turn from sin, Lord, grant heaven - ly grace.

Save me, Lord, I cry. In your cross I trust,
Raised up and re - newed, may I fol - low you,

In the early 20th century, it was often said in China 'One Christian more means one Chinese less.' The use of an ancient Confucian chant in worship is one way in which Chinese Christians are able to root their faith in their Chinese culture and traditions.

Je - sus, Son of God, ho - ly, bless - èd one.
Je - sus, Son of God, ho - ly, bless - èd one.

1 Lord, forgive me. Christ, have mercy!
I confess to you all my sin and shame.
Save me, Lord, I cry.
In your cross I trust,
Jesus, Son of God, holy, blessèd one.

2 Lord, forgive me. Christ, have mercy!
Now to turn from sin, Lord,
    grant heavenly grace.
Raised up and renewed,
may I follow you,
Jesus, Son of God, holy, blessèd one.

97 LORD, AS I WAKE I TURN TO YOU

IRELAND

Words: Brian Foley
Music: Irish traditional melody
arranged Geoff Weaver

1 Lord, as I wake I turn to you, yourself the
2 There is no bless - ing, Lord, from you for those who
3 Your lov - ing gifts of grace to me, those fav - ours
4 Lord, make my life a life of love, keep me from

first thought of my day; my king, my God, whose help is
make their will their way, no praise for those who will not
I could ne - ver earn, call for my thanks in praise and
sin in all I do; Lord, make your law my on - ly

sure, your - self the help for which I pray.
praise, no peace for those who will not pray.
prayer, call me to love you in re - turn.
law, your will my will, for love of you.

A little known and haunting Irish melody
provides an appropriate setting of Psalm 5.

98 MAJESTET, KONGE I EVIGHET
Majesty, King of eternity

Words and music: Jan Honningdal
English: Word & Music
arranged David Peacock

NORWAY

A recent worship song from Norway which needs to be 'held-back' rather than rushed.

Majestet, Konge i evighet,
Jord og hav og himmel,
 alt er skapt av deg.
Majestet, Konge i evighet,
du, en borg til frelse,
et sikkert skjulested.
 Vi vil opphøye deg, Kong Jesus.
 Hvert et kne skal bøye seg for deg.
 Vi vil opphøye deg, Kong Jesus.
 Ingen er som du,
 nei, ingen er som du.

Majesty, King of eternity –
earth and sea and heaven,
 all are your design.
Majesty, King of eternity –
you're our strength and refuge,
you're our hiding-place.
 We will adore you, King Jesus –
 every knee shall bow
 before your throne;
we will adore you, King Jesus –
there is none like you,
no, there is none like you.

99 MAR SHA ÍSÁ
My Saviour

PAKISTAN

Words: from the Pushto, Alison Blenkinsop
Music: unknown
arranged Geoff Weaver

Flowing ♩ = 60

Lyrics:

Mar sha Í - sá___ pa á - zá - ra za - má da -
-pá - ra, marg da Ma - síh___ de. My Sav - iour
met___ death's op - pres - sion for my trans -
-gres - sion, for___ me he suf - fered.

> An intense prayer in song, based on Isaac Watts' 'When I survey the wondrous cross', from the small, beleaguered Christian community on the North West frontier of Pakistan. Allow a free and easy rhythmic flow.

Verse

1 When I con - si - der the won-drous sto - ry of Je-sus'
2 I can no lon - ger find sel - fish plea - sure in all that
3 His ve - ry life - blood was poured out free - ly, his sac - ri -

death on the cross of glo - ry, I give re -
late - ly I used to trea - sure; I free - ly
- fice has the power to heal me; in death he

- pent - ance ex - pres - sion for my trans -
make this con - fes - sion of my trans -
made in - ter - ces - sion for my trans -

_D.S._

- gres - sion — for me he suf - fered.
- gres - sion — for me he suf - fered.
- gres - sion — for me he suf - fered. My Sav - iour

100

MAW HEE MA
Glory to God

NEPAL

Words: unknown
Music: unknown
arranged Geoff Weaver

Lively waltz tempo ♩. = 56

Maw hee ma, maw hee ma, maw he ma hoass.
Dunn ya baad, dunn ya baad, dunn ya baad hoass.
Pra shunn sa, pra shunn sa, pra shunn sa hoass.
Glo - ry to God, give the glo - ry to him!
Thanks be to God, give the thanks now to him!
Praise be to God, give the praise now to him!

Maw hee ma, maw hee ma, maw he ma hoass.
Dunn ya baad, dunn ya baad, dunn ya baad hoass.
Pra shunn sa, pra shunn sa, pra shunn sa hoass.
Glo - ry to God, give the glo - ry to him!
Thanks be to God, give the thanks now to him!
Praise be to God, give the praise now to him!

Eesh wor - ra laa ee_____ maw hee ma__ hoass,
Eesh wor - ra laa ee_____ dunn ya baad_ hoass,
Eesh wor - ra laa ee_____ pra shunn sa__ hoass,
Come, let us sing,_____ 'Glo - ry to__ God,
Come, let us sing,_____ 'Thanks be to__ God,
Come, let us sing,_____ 'Praise be to__ God,

A simple chorus, waltz-like in character, from Nepal. Until recently many Christians were imprisoned for their faith in Nepal. As so often in these circumstances, the church there has grown rapidly, and has rejoiced in a recent easing of restrictions.

Music arrangement: © 1995 Geoff Weaver / Jubilate Hymns   Words: Nepali and English Copyright control

Maw hee ma, maw hee ma,
maw he ma hoass.
Maw hee ma, maw hee ma,
maw hee ma hoass.
Eesh worra laa ee
    maw hee ma hoass,
    maw hee ma hoass.

Dunn ya baad, dunn ya baad,
dunn ya baad hoass.
Dunn ya baad . . .
Eesh worra laa ee
    dunn ya baad hoass,
    dunn ya baad hoass.

Pra shunn sa, pra shunn sa,
pra shunn sa hoass.
Pra shunn sa . . .
Eesh worra laa ee
    pra shunn sa hoass,
    pra shunn sa hoass.

Glory to God, give the glory to him!
Glory to God, give the glory to him!
Come, let us sing,
  'Glory to God,
  glory to God!'

Thanks be to God, give the thanks now to him!
Thanks be to God, give the thanks now to him!
Come, let us sing,
  'Thanks be to God,
  thanks be to God!'

Praise be to God, give the praise now to him!
Praise be to God, give the praise now to him!
Come, let us sing,
  'Praise be to God,
  praise be to God!'

101 MAY THE PEACE OF GOD THE FATHER

ISRAEL

Words: unknown
in this version Word & Music
Music: Israeli melody
arranged David Peacock

Flowing ♩ = 74

A May the peace of God the Fa - ther   B and the grace of Christ, the
Son,   A with the bless-ing of the Spi - rit -
B God the ho - ly Three-in - One: A be up - on you
al-ways, and re-main   B now and ev - er   with you. A-men.

> This haunting modal song of blessing is most effective when
> sung by two groups: the one responding to the other.

102 MOTO UMEWAKA LEO
God's fire

EAST AFRICA

Words and music: unknown
arranged Geoff Weaver

Lively ♩ = 108

Mo - to u - me - wa - ka le - o, *Mo - to ni*
God's fire is burn-ing in my soul, God's fire has

ka - zi ya Ye - su, *Mo - to u - me - wa - ka le - o;* *Tu-*
come to make me whole, God's fire is sweep-ing through the earth; praise

-im - be hal - le - lu - jah___ mo - to u - me - wa - ka! *Tu-*
God, I've got God's fire and___ it's burn-ing in my soul! Praise

-im - be hal - le - lu - jah___ mo - to u - me - wa - ka!
God — yes, hal - le - lu - jah___ it's burn-ing in my soul!

A song which most probably came out of the East African revival.
It needs to be sung with rhythm, fire and commitment.

103 MAYENZIWE 'NTANDO YAKHO
Your will be done on earth

SOUTH AFRICA

Words: from the Lord's Prayer
Music: transcribed by John L. Bell

Not too fast ♩ = 96

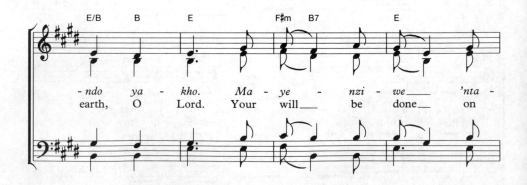

> A traditional song from South Africa, joyful and affirmative. This is best sung *a cappella*.

-ndo___ ya - kho.___ Ma - ye - nzi - we 'nta - ndo ya -
earth,___ O Lord._ Your will be done on earth, O___

- kho. Ma - ye - nzi - we 'nta - ndo ya - kho.
Lord. Your will be done on earth, O Lord.

Mayenziwe 'ntando yakho.
Mayenziwe 'ntando yakho.
Mayenziwe 'ntando yakho.
Mayenziwe 'ntando yakho.
Mayenziwe 'ntando yakho.

Your will be done on earth, O Lord.
Your will be done on earth, O Lord.
Your will be done on earth, O Lord.
Your will be done on earth, O Lord.
Your will be done on earth, O Lord.

104 MFURAHINI, HALLELUYA
He has arisen, alleluia!

TANZANIA

Words: Bernard Kyamanywa
Howard S. Olson
Music: unknown
arranged Geoff Weaver

1 M - fu - ra - hi - ni, hal - le - lu - ya m - ko - mbo -
2 A - me - fu - fu - ka M - ko - mbo - zi hal - le - lu -
1 He has a - ris - en, al - le - lu - ia! Re - joice and
2 For three long days the grave did its worst un - til its

- zi a - me - fu - fu - ka. A - me - fu - fu - ka,
- ya, tu - sha - ngi - li - e. Ngu - vu za mwo - vu
praise him, al - le - lu - ia! For our Re - deem - er
strength by God was dis - persed. He who gives life did

hal - le - lu - ya. M - si - fu - ni sa - sa yu ha - i.
a - me - shi - nda. A - me - tu - on - do - a ku - fa - ni.
burst from the tomb – e - ven from death, dis - pell - ing its gloom.
death un - der - go, and in its con - quest his might did show.

A traditional dance-like Tanzanian song which needs to move at a lively one in a bar. The leader-congregation format is typically African. The song would be enhanced by appropriate drum rhythms.

Chorus ALL (HARMONY)

Tu - mwi - mbi - e so - te kwa fu - ra - ha. Ye - su a -
Let us sing praise to him with end - less joy: death's fear - ful

- me - to - ka ka - bu - ri - ni. Ka - shin - da Ki - fo,
sting he has come to des - troy, our sins for - giv - ing,

hal - le - lu - ya. Hal - le - lu - ya, Ye - su yu ha - i.
al - le - lu - ia! Je - sus is liv - ing, al - le - lu - ia!

3 Malaika aliwaambia
   wanawake, 'Msiogope.
   Sasa kaburi lipo tupu
   kwani Yesu amefufuka.'
      Tumwimbie sote . . .

3 The angel said to them, 'Do not fear;
   you look for Jesus – he is not here.
   See for yourselves, the tomb is all bare,
   only the grave-clothes are lying there.'
      Let us sing . . .

4 'Amebatilisha Shetani.
   Amewaletea wokovu.
   Kwa hiyo ninyi mtangaze
   ni hakika, Yesu yu hai.'
      Tumwimbie sote . . .

4 'Go spread the news, he's not in the grave:
   he has arisen, mighty to save.
   Jesus' redeeming labours are done –
   even the battle with sin is won.'
      Let us sing . . .

105 MWAMBA NI JESU
Who is the Rock

EAST AFRICA

Words and music: J. Nathan Corbitt

Confidently ♩ = 120

Capo 3(D)

SOLO 1 *Mwam-ba, Mwam-ba?*_____
Who is the Rock?_____

(only on repeat) ALL *Mwam-ba ni Je-su, Mwam-ba.*_____
The Rock is Je-sus, the Rock._____

D.C.

*Mwam-ba, Mwam-ba?*_____
Who is the Rock?_____

*Mwam-ba ni Je-su, Mwam-ba.*_____
The Rock is Je-sus, the Rock._____

A song in the African call-response tradition. No books are required for the congregation and the song can be extended indefinitely as the soloist recalls the different attributes of Jesus the Rock.

1	SOLO	*Mwamba, Mwamba?*	1	SOLO	Who is the Rock?
	ALL	*Mwamba ni Jesu, Mwamba.*		ALL	The Rock is Jesus, the Rock.
	SOLO	*Mwamba, Mwamba?*		SOLO	Who is the Rock?
	ALL	*Mwamba ni Jesu, Mwamba.*		ALL	The Rock is Jesus, the Rock.

1 SOLO *Mwamba, Mwamba?*
   ALL   *Mwamba ni Jesu, Mwamba.*
   SOLO *Mwamba, Mwamba?*
   ALL   *Mwamba ni Jesu, Mwamba.*

2 SOLO *Abariki:*
   ALL   *Mwamba ni Jesu, Mwamba.*
   SOLO *Abariki:*
   ALL   *Mwamba ni Jesu, Mwamba.*

3 SOLO *Anaponya:*
   ALL   *Mwamba ni Jesu, Mwamba.*
   SOLO *Anaponya:*
   ALL   *Mwamba ni Jesu, Mwamba.*

4 SOLO *Analinda:*
   ALL   *Mwamba ni Jesu, Mwamba.*
   SOLO *Analinda:*
   ALL   *Mwamba ni Jesu, Mwamba.*

5 SOLO *Aokoa:*
   ALL   *Mwamba ni Jesu, Mwamba.*
   SOLO *Aokoa:*
   ALL   *Mwamba ni Jesu, Mwamba.*

6 SOLO *Mwamba . . .*

7 SOLO *Mwamba . . .*

1 SOLO Who is the Rock?
   ALL   The Rock is Jesus, the Rock.
   SOLO Who is the Rock?
   ALL   The Rock is Jesus, the Rock.

2 SOLO He blesses us:
   ALL   the Rock is Jesus, the Rock.
   SOLO He blesses us:
   ALL   the Rock is Jesus, the Rock.

3 SOLO He heals from sin:
   ALL   the Rock is Jesus, the Rock.
   SOLO He heals from sin:
   ALL   the Rock is Jesus, the Rock.

4 SOLO The Rock protects:
   ALL   the Rock is Jesus, the Rock.
   SOLO The Rock protects:
   ALL   the Rock is Jesus, the Rock.

5 SOLO He rescues us:
   ALL   the Rock is Jesus, the Rock.
   SOLO He rescues us:
   ALL   the Rock is Jesus, the Rock.

6 SOLO Who is the Rock . . .

7 SOLO Who is the Rock . . .

106 MY SOUL WILL GLORIFY

INDONESIA

Words: from Luke 1
D. T. Niles
Music: Maluku popular song
arranged Geoff Weaver

Dance-like ♩. = 72

Capo 3(Bm)

1 My soul will glo-ri-fy the Lord, my spi-rit will re-
2 Re-joice for ev-er at my name, for God has done great
3 The proud he scat-ters in their pride, the rich must emp-ty

-joice; for my Re-deem-er has looked down and
things, and ho-ly is the one who came the
go; the strong his strength has set a-side, the

made my life his choice. God's will-ing ser-vant
sav-iour, King of kings. The mer-cy of our
might-y are brought low. The hum-ble will yet

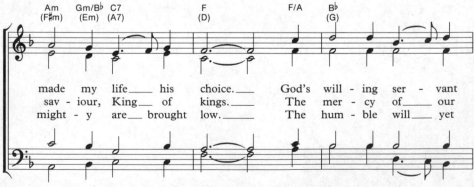

This captures beautifully the joy and the dance-like character
of Mary's song. Ideally it should be sung unaccompanied.

I'll be-come the mo-ther of the Christ, and
God is great, and sure his deeds of love; he
high ap-pear, the poor be filled with food; the

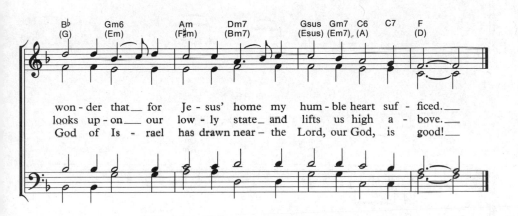

won-der that for Je-sus' home my hum-ble heart suf-ficed.
looks up-on our low-ly state and lifts us high a-bove.
God of Is-rael has drawn near – the Lord, our God, is good!

1 My soul will glorify the Lord,
my spirit will rejoice;
for my Redeemer has looked down
and made my life his choice.
God's willing servant I'll become –
the mother of the Christ,
and wonder that for Jesus' home
my humble heart sufficed.

2 Rejoice for ever at my name,
for God has done great things,
and holy is the one who came –
the saviour, King of kings.
The mercy of our God is great,
and sure his deeds of love;
he looks upon our lowly state
and lifts us high above.

3 The proud he scatters in their pride,
the rich must empty go;
the strong his strength has set aside,
the mighty are brought low.
The humble will yet high appear,
the poor be filled with food;
the God of Israel has drawn near –
the Lord, our God, is good!

107 MY PRAYERS RISE

UNITED STATES OF AMERICA

Words: from Psalm 141: 2
Arlo D. Duba
Music: Arlo D. Duba
arranged Geoff Weaver

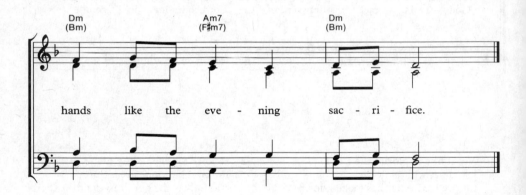

My prayers rise like incense,
my hands like the evening sacrifice.

This simple response was first sung as part of a service for justice, peace and the integrity of creation. It can be used effectively within a time of prayer.

108 NA JIJOHO
Peace be with you

BENIN

Words: traditional
Music: unknown
arranged Geoff Weaver

This song is very popular in Benin and is sung at thanksgiving and indeed on almost any occasion. It is simple enough to sing as greetings, or as the Peace is exchanged.

109 NGAIH CHIAT TAHNAK KA TON LID AH
When I am sad and sorrowful

MYANMAR

Words: unknown
in this version Word & Music
Music: unknown
arranged David Peacock

Lilting ♩ = 108

Ngaih chiat tah - nak ka ton lid ah,   *a ka hnum tu*
When I am sad and sor - row - ful,   Je - sus is there;

hawi tha bik cu Je - suh a si_____
he's my best friend, my Sa - viour._____

dwat mi hna nih thlan mual ran - liam   lid can zon - gah
When all my friends have gone a - way,   in that sad day,

bawi Je - suh nih a ka um - pi._____
Je - sus my Lord is with___ me._____ More

The recent history of Myanmar (Burma) has been one of great oppression and suffering. The editor recently met a young man who dared not return home to his family and this song was sung to him by another radical young Christian who feared for the future of his country. Many families have lost loved ones and the words of this song must be truly heartfelt.

110 NEEMA, NEEMA
Spirit of Jesus

EAST AFRICA

Words and music: unknown
arranged Geoff Weaver

Nee - ma, nee - ma, nee - ma i - me fu - nel - wa.
Spi - rit of Je - sus – Ho - ly Spi - rit, come to us.
Grace of the Fa - ther – Ho - ly Spi - rit, come to us.

Neema, neema,
neema ime funelwa.

Spirit of Jesus – Holy Spirit, come to us.
Grace of the Father – Holy Spirit, come to us.

> A simple affirmation in song, ideal for a congregational response.

111 NAGRIKUDZWE ZUVA
Come, let us celebrate the day

ZIMBABWE

Words: from the Zimbabwean
in this version Word & Music
Music: Abraham Maraire

Exuberantly ♩. = 125

Verse

1 Nag - ri - ku-dzwe zu - va   i - ro a - no-mu - ka.
2 Ru - fa - ro ku - ne ma-ko - re   a - ke.
3 Kri - si - tu zvi-sho-ma kwa - ti - ri wa - pi - wa.
4 Zvi - no   u - no-pi - nda ma - te-nga ku-mu - so - ro.

1 Come, let   us ce - le - brate the   day of Je-sus' ri - sing.
2 For he has re - con - ciled us   to   the   Fa - ther.
3 To earth he came in   love   to   be   our   bro - ther.
4 Now high - ex - al - ted he   is   yet   a - mong us.

Chorus

Ha - le - lu - ja,   ha - le - lu - ja!
Hal - le - lu - jah,   hal - le - lu - jah!

Final Chorus

Ha - le - lu - ja,   ha - le - lu - ja,
Hal-le - lu - jah,   hal-le - lu-jah,

- lu - ja,   - lu - ja,   ha - le - lu - ja,   ha - le - lu - ja!
- lu-jah,   - lu-jah,   hal-le - lu - jah,   hal-le - lu-jah!

An exuberant Easter song which is enhanced by rhythmic accompaniment as follows:

Verse ‖: ♫♫ ♫♫ ♫ ♫ ♫ :‖   First Chorus ‖: ♩ ♩ ♩ ♩♪ ♪♩ :‖

Final Chorus ‖: ♩ ♫♩ ♩ ♫♩ :‖

The final chorus can be taken out of context and used in a variety of ways.

112 NKOSI SIKELEL' IAFRIKA
Lord, bless Africa

SOUTH AFRICA

Words: verse 1 Enoch Mankayi Sontonga
verse 2 unknown
Music: unknown

With dignity ♩ = 96

Nko-si si-ke-lel' i - A - fri - ka Ma-lu-pha-kan-yi-sw' u - pho-ndo lwa - yo____ Yi-zwa i - mi-than-da - zo ye-thu

Nko - si si-ke-le - la,____ 1 nko-si____ si-ke-le - la.
2 Thi - na lu-sa-pho lwa - yo.

si-ke-le - la Nko-si si-ke-le - la si-ke-le -

Wo - za Mo-ya   Wo - za Mo-ya

This song carries so many resonances and memories for all who struggled for a democratic South Africa. It remains a powerful prayer for those who lead the new order in that country where suffering and hope have gone hand in hand. Feel the richness and nobility of the harmony. The first verse was composed in 1897 by Enoch Mankayi Sontonga, a Christian musician from Cape Province.

Music: © Dave Dargie

Words: verse 1 © Enoch Mankayi Sontonga / Copyright control
verse 2 Copyright control

LITERAL TRANSLATION*

Lord, bless Africa,
let its horn be raised,
listen also to our prayers.
Lord, bless us –
we, the family of Africa.

Come, Spirit;
come, Holy Spirit.

Lord bless us – we, the family of Africa.

Lord, bless our nation,
stop wars and suffering,
save it, Lord.
Our nation,
the African nation,
let it be so for ever.

* this does not fit the music

PRONUNCIATION
'u' pron. 'oo'.
'ph' pron. 'p'.

'th' pron. 't'.
'c' pron. as a 'tut' sound.
'a' pron. 'ah'.

113 O LORD, HEAR MY PRAYER

FRANCE

Words: from Psalm 130
Music: Jacques Berthier

This Taizé chant has travelled throughout the world. It may be appropriate at times to change the text to 'O Lord hear *our* prayer'.

114 ODI, ODI
We're told he was born at a Bethlehem inn

MALAWI

Words: Tom Colvin
Music: Malawi dance tune
adapted Tom Colvin
arranged Geoff Weaver

Brightly ♩. = 60

Capo 3(D)   Verse

UNISON 1 We're told he was born at a Beth-le-hem inn, where
HARMONY 2 He comes now— a stran-ger who asks for our aid, he
HARMONY 4 He comes as a bro-ther, he comes as a friend, he
UNISON 5 Lord Je-sus, you're wel-come, the door's o-pen wide; we

Jo-seph and Ma-ry had begged to get in; for birth-place a sta-ble was
comes in dis-guise that he might per-suade; he comes to us ear-ly, he
comes all our ha-tred and war-fare to end; he comes to u-nite and he
beg you to en-ter and with us a-bide: your love in our heart and your

all they could find al-though he was God's gift to all of our kind.
comes to us late, and hum-bly he waits and he cries at our gate.
comes to re-store, but— al-ways so hum-bly— he calls at our door.
smile on our face, we'll see you in stran-gers who stand in your place.

Chorus

v.1 UNISON MEN
vv.2,3,4 HARMONY

'O-di, o-di!' a stran-ger has come! 'O-

> 'Odi' means 'hello'. The harmonies are best realised *a cappella* and
> a single drum beat helps to maintain a gentle two in a bar feel. This
> arrangement gives opportunity for plenty of textural variety.

- di, o - di! Will you wel-come me here?' 'O - di, o - di! I

last time **to Coda** ✛

stand here and wait.' 'O - di, o - di! Will you o - pen your gate?'

Verse 3 *lower parts hum*

3 He comes as a ser - vant to black and to white, and

shows us the way that we all may u - nite; he of - fers his friend-ship to

115 OH, ISN'T IT GOOD
Perfect harmony

BLACK GOSPEL

Words and music: Howard Francis
and Wayne Wilson

Oh, is-n't it good_ to be as one,_ liv-ing in per - fect har-mo-ny,

_ shar - ing the good_ things_ God_ has done, God_ has done?_

Coming from a Black Gospel tradition, this ecstatic song requires
rhythmic freedom and a wide range of emotional expression.

Chorus

Oh, is-n't it good to be as one, liv-ing in per-

-fect har-mo-ny, shar-ing the good things God

repeat chorus ad lib.

has done, God has done? Ooh.

116 ON THE MOUNTAIN

NIGERIA

Words and music: collected Geoff Weaver
arranged Geoff Weaver

On the moun-tain,_ in the val-ley,_ on the land and in the sea; on the moun-tain, in the val-ley,_ on the land and in the sea, hal-le-lu-jah! My

The Igbo Christians of Eastern Nigeria have many short songs of affirmation. This, with words partly drawn from the Psalms, reaffirms God's presence and goodness in all situations.

On the mountain, in the valley,
on the land and in the sea;
on the mountain, in the valley,
on the land and in the sea, hallelujah!

My God is my portion
in the land of the living;
my God is good for evermore.
My God is my portion
in the land of the living;
my God is good for evermore.

117 OUR FATHER WHO IS IN HEAVEN

CARIBBEAN

Words: Lord's Prayer
Music: unknown
arranged David Peacock

This well known Caribbean setting of the Lord's Prayer can be sung very effectively as a solo-response song, with the congregation singing the refrain 'Hallowed be your name', preferably in simple harmonies as suggested.

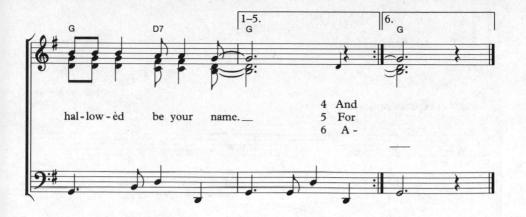

hal-low-èd   be your   name.___

4 And
5 For
6 A -

1 Our Father who is in heaven,
   hallowèd be your name,
   your kingdom come, your will be done,
   hallowèd be your name.

2 On earth as it is in heaven,
   hallowèd be your name,
   give us this day our daily bread,
   hallowèd be your name.

3 Forgive us all our trespasses,
   hallowèd be your name,
   as we forgive those who trespass against us,
   hallowèd be your name.

4 And lead us not into temptation,
   hallowèd be your name,
   but deliver us from all that is evil,
   hallowèd be your name.

5 For yours is the kingdom, the power and the glory,
   hallowèd be your name,
   for ever and for ever,
   hallowèd be your name.

6 Amen, amen, amen, amen,
   hallowèd be your name,
   amen, amen, amen, amen,
   hallowèd be your name.

118 OUVE, SENHOR
Merciful Lord

BRAZIL

Words: S. Monteiro
English: Word & Music
Music: unknown
arranged David Peacock

With expression ♩ = 84

Ou-ve, Se-nhor, eu es-tou cla-man-do,
Mer-ci-ful Lord, in your lov-ing-kind-ness

tem pie-da-de de mim e me res-pon-de.
hear our prayer, lis-ten to our in-ter-ces-sion.

Ou-ve, Se-nhor, eu es-tou cla-man-do,
Mer-ci-ful Lord, in your lov-ing-kind-ness

tem pie-da-de de mim e me res-pon-de.
hear our prayer, lis-ten to our in-ter-ces-sion.

An impassioned plea, suitable for times of prayer, in a very Brazilian idiom.

VOCAL HARMONY accompaniment

Sing to 'Ooh' throughout

119 ONYAME KOKROKO
Great God of power and might

GHANA

Words and music: Dinah Reindorf
arranged Geoff Weaver

Onyame Kokroko!
Onyame Kokroko!
Onyame Kokroko!
Onyame Kokroko!
Abodze nyina kotow luo, Onyame Kokroko!
Abodze nyina kotow luo, Onyame Kokroko!

Great God of power and might,
great God of power and might,
great God of power and might,
great God of power and might,
creation bows down at your name,
great God of power and might.
Creation bows down at your name,
great God of power and might.

Don't be put off by the apparent rhythmic complexity, and don't be afraid to literally bow down 'with all creation'. A good example of a worship in action song.

120 PACIENTEMENTE
Patiently waiting for you

Words: from Psalm 40, unknown
in this version Word & Music
Music: Chilean melody
arranged David Peacock

With expression ♩ = 107

Pa - cien-te-men-te es-per - é a Je-ho - vá — y se in-cli-nó ha - cia mi.

Pa - tient-ly wait-ing for you, O Lord – you lis-ten to my prayer;

Pa - cien - te - men - te es-per - é a Je-ho - vá — y se in-cli-nó ha - cia mí.

pa - tient-ly wait-ing for you, O Lord – you lis-ten to my prayer.

Me hi-zo sac-ar del po - zo___ de la des-es-per - a-ción,___

Out of the pit you pulled___ me,___ out___ of the mud and mire,

This melody has three distinct sections through which the song needs to build.

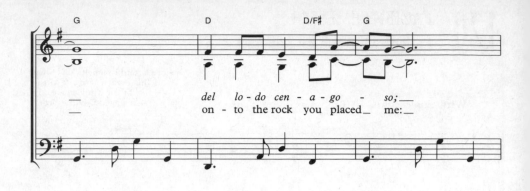

del lo - do cen - a - go - so;
on - to the rock you placed_ me:_

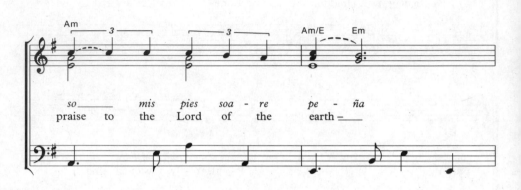

_so___ mis pies so a - re pe - ña_
praise to the Lord of the earth =_

_y en - de - re - zo mis___ pa - sos.___
you gave my mouth a_____ new_____ song!_

Pus - o lue - go en mi bo - ca cán - ti - co
Blessed are you__ if you trust the Lord_ God; for

nue-vo, al - a - ban-za a nuestro Dios;   *pus - o lue - go en mi*
ma-ny are the won-ders he has done: praise the Lord – he has

bo - ca cán - ti - co   *nue - vo, a - la - ban-za a nues - tro*
brought sal - va - tion, sing   'Al - le - lu - ia! Glo - ry to the

Dios,   *a - la - ban-za a nues-tro Dios.*
Lord;   al - le - lu - ia to the Lord!'

Pacientemente esperé a Jehová	Patiently waiting for you, O Lord –
y se inclinó hacia mí	you listen to my prayer;
Pacientemente esperé a Jehová	patiently waiting for you, O Lord –
y se inclinó hacia mí.	you listen to my prayer.
Me hizo sacar del pozo	Out of the pit you pulled me,
de la desesperación,	out of the mud and mire,
del lodo cenagoso;	onto the rock you placed me:
so mis pies soare peña	praise to the Lord of the earth –
y enderezo mis pasos.	you gave my mouth a new song!
Puso luego en mi boca cántico nuevo,	Blessed are you if you trust the Lord God;
alabanza a nuestro Dios;	for many are the wonders he has done:
puso luego en mi boca cántico nuevo,	praise the Lord – he has brought salvation,
alabanza a nuestro Dios,	sing 'Alleluia! Glory to the Lord;
alabanza a nuestro Dios.	alleluia to the Lord!'

121 PORQUE DIOS SE HIZO
Jesus Christ, the hope of the world

ARGENTINA

Words and music: Pablo Bedrossian
English: From John 14, Michael Perry
music arranged David Peacock

With a swing ♩ = 115

1 Por - que Dios se hi - zo hom - bre___ y
1 Je - sus Christ, the hope___ of the___ world, you

nos mos - tró___ su a - mor, nos en - se - ñó___ có -
died that we___ might live; in love you came to

- mo vi - vir,___ y nos dio___ u - na mi - sión; y___
bear our shame and you taught us how to for - give: then you

por nues-tros___ pe - ca - dos en___ u - na cruz mu - rió___
rose from death's do - min - ion and you reign in high - est heaven;

A song specially composed for the Baptist World Alliance World Congress held in
Buenos Aires in July 1995. It reflects the theme 'Christ – the hope of the world'.

Words and music: © Pablo Bedrossian /
Asociacion Bautista Argentina de Publicaciones

English words: © 1995 Michael Perry / Jubilate Hymns

-jem - plo   que Je - sús nos de - jó.
glo - ry   and we praise you to - day!

INSTRUMENTAL LINK AND ENDING

2   *Porque aunque los tiempos cambian,*
    él nunca cambiará;
    y su misericordia fiel a todos quiere alcanzar.
    A los que sufren violencia, a los que no tienen pan,
    a cada hombre de esta tierra, él nos envía ya.
      Celebremos a Cristo . . .

2   Jesus Christ, the hope of the world,
    your grace will never fail,
    though powers of hell may wreck or kill,
    yet your kingdom will prevail;
    for you hold the sword of justice
    and the nations wait for peace,
    you'll come at last to take us home –
    all hail, Redeemer, hail!
      Celebrate the Messiah . . .

122 PRABHOO LAYLAY
O Lord Jesus, enfold me in your arms

PAKISTAN

Words: Samuel Paul,
paraphrased Shirley Murray
Music: Samuel Paul
arranged Geoff Weaver

Chorus

Pra-bhoo Lay-lay muj-hay Too Ba-hoñ Meñ ka-heen
O Lord Je-sus, en-fold me in your arms, let me

gir - na ja - aun gu-naa-hon meñ.
ne - ver be part - ed from your love;

Verse

1 Me - ra tan man aur dhan te-ray lee - ay, me-ra
2 Me - ray dil ko too ap - nay ruh say bhar me-ray
3 Pa - ape e - on ko main laau te-ray pass ab - di
1 All my be - ing and all that I poss - ess, all my
2 Let your Spi - rit be al - ways in my heart, and let
3 Let me bring to you oth - ers who are lost — in their

1.

sa - ra jee - van te ray lee - ay.
dil ho se - raf te - ra ni ghar.
ku - shi pa - en jo hain ud aas.
life is com - mit - ted to you, Lord;
on - ly your Spi - rit live with - in;
sad - ness, may they dis - co - ver joy;

An unusual stylistic blend of syncopated rhythms with words of
deep personal commitment. The verses may be sung as solos.

123 PURIHIN ANG PANGINOON
Give praise to the Lord

PHILIPPINES

Words: from Psalms 149 and 150, F. Ll. Ramirez,
paraphrased Beth Nacion-Puyot and James Minchin
Music: F. Ll. Ramirez
arranged David Peacock

Joyfully ♩. = 52

Pu - ri - hin ang Pa - ngi - no - on,_____ u -
Give praise to the Lord, all the earth,_____ in

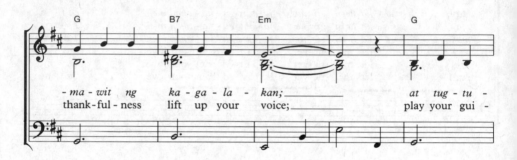

-ma - wit ng ka - ga - la - kan;_____ at tug - tu -
thank - ful - ness lift up your voice;_____ play your gui -

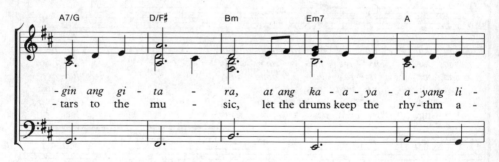

-gin ang gi - ta - ra, at ang ka - a - ya - a - yang li -
-tars to the mu - sic, let the drums keep the rhy - thm a -

Fine

- ra,_____ hi - pan nin - yo ang trom - pe - ta.
- live,_____ with trum - pet and or - gan re - joice.

Like many of the psalms, this song reaffirms the importance of praise and thanksgiving in the midst of troubles. Filipino Christians know a great deal about troubles and burdens, but still manage to sing with great joy and vigour.

1 Sa a - ting pag - ka - ba - ga - bag,
2 Ang pa - sa - ning ma - bi - gat,_____
3 Ka - ya't Pa - ngin - oo'y ding - gin, and

1 When you are bo - thered by trou - bles,
2 E - ven the loads and the bur - dens
3 We must o - bey God's com - mand - ments,

sa Diyos ta - yo'y tu - ma - wag;_____
sa 'ting ma - nga ba - li - kat,_____
lan - das N' - ya'y ta - ha - kin,_____

seek the Lord's com - fort - ing words:_____
you find too hea - vy to bear =_____
fol - low the path we are shown;_____

sa a - ting ma - nga ka - a - way ta - yo
pi - na - ga - an nang lu - bu - san ng Di -
ha - bam - bu - hay ay pu - ri - hin, ka - ga -

from all your foes you'll be shield - ed, he will
each one is light - ened by Je - sus, the Re -
and ev - ery mo - ment with prais - es we'll pro -

ay Kan - yang i - ni - lig - tas._____ Pu -
- yos na ta - ga - pag - lig - tas._____ Pu -
- nda - hang - loob N' - ya sa 'tin._____ Pu -

al - ways be there for your good._____ Give
- deem - er and Sav - iour of all._____ Give
- claim the Lord's deeds to the world._____ Give

124 QINGCHEN ZAO
God, be praised at early morn

CHINA

Words and music: Dawei Wang
arranged Geoff Weaver
alternative arrangement Pen-li Chen

1 Qing-chen_ zao qi can-mei_ Shen, yi-ye_ ping-an
1 God, be_ praised at ear-ly_ morn for pro - tect-ing

meng_ Shen en,_ Jin-ri_ hai qiu Zhu bao-
me_ at night:_ on this_ day, and as I_

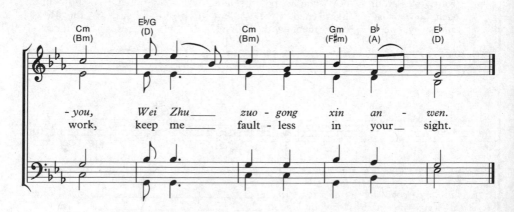

- you, Wei Zhu_ zuo-gong xin an - wen.
work, keep me_ fault - less in your_ sight.

This song of thanksgiving for safe-keeping is based upon an ancient Chinese folksong.

UNISON

1 Qing-chen zao qi can-mei_ Shen,   yi - ye_ ping-an
1 God, be_ praised at ear-ly_ morn   for pro-tect-ing

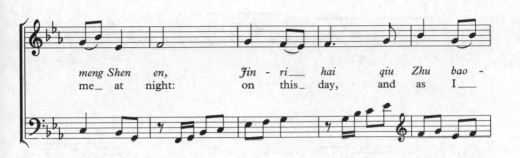

meng Shen en,   Jin - ri_ hai   qiu Zhu bao -
me_ at night: on this_ day,   and as I_

- you,   Wei Zhu____ zuo - gong xin an - wen.
work,   keep me____ fault - less in your sight.

1   Qingchen zao qi canmei Shen,
    yiye pingan meng Shen en,
    Jinri hai qiu Zhu baoyou,
    Wei Zhu zuogong xin anwen.

1   God, be praised at early morn
    for protecting me at night:
    on this day, and as I work,
    keep me faultless in your sight.

2   Shen di rong-guang zhao si-fang,
    Chong-man yu-zhou he hui-huang,
    zhen guang zhao zai wo xin shang,
    Shen en hou ai chang song-yang.

2   God, your glory's radiant beam
    fills the universe with grace,
    shines its light within my heart –
    in your mercy, hear my praise.

3   Qi-qiu Sheng-ling shi da-neng,
    Qu wo zui-i huan xin-ren,
    Qian-bei wen-rou xiao-fa Zhu,
    Ha-li-lu-ya rong-yao Shen.

3   By your power, O Spirit blessed,
    cleanse me from my sins anew;
    faithful Master, whom I trust,
    let me pledge my love to you.

125 RABB KI HOWE SANA HAMESHA
Sing the Lord's praises for ever

PAKISTAN

Words: from Psalm 150,
translated Alison Blenkinsop
Music: unknown
arranged Geoff Weaver

Fast and lively ♩ = 126

Rabb-(a) ki ho - we__ sa-na ha-me-sha, rabb-(a) ki ho-we__

sa - na._____ Sing the Lord's prai - ses for

ev-er and ev - er;__ sing the Lord's prai - ses for ev-er._____

An exuberant Hindi setting of Psalm 150. A performance will be enhanced by the use of rhythmic percussion and echo effects as suggested. Some pronunciation helps are:
Rabb has a little vowel after it – like 'rubber'
ki = key
howe = no way (slight 'v' sound to the 'w')
sana = sun-nah
hamesha = hu-may-sha

Rabb-(a) ki ho - we___ sa - na.___

Rabb ki howe sana hamesha,
rabb ki howe sana.
Sing the Lord's praises for ever and ever;
sing the Lord's praises for ever.

1   Let us praise the Lord with our voices,
    let us praise the Lord with our voices,
    praising his name for ever and ever,
    praising his name for ever, *hamesha.*
        Rabb ki howe sana.
        Sing the Lord's praises . . .

2   Let us praise the Lord in his temple,
    let us praise the Lord in his temple,
    thanking and praising the Lord for ever,
    thanking and praising the Lord, *hamesha.*
        Rabb ki howe sana.
        Sing the Lord's praises . . .

3   For he is the mighty creator,
    for he is the mighty creator:
    tell of his glory and power for ever,
    tell of his glory and power, *hamesha.*
        Rabb ki howe sana.
        Sing the Lord's praises . . .

4   Loudly play the horns and the trumpets,
    loudly play the horns and the trumpets;
    play on the lute and the pipes together,
    play on the lute and the pipes, *hamesha.*
        Rabb ki howe sana.
        Sing the Lord's praises . . .

5   Play with skill the violin and 'cello,
    play with skill the violin and 'cello;
    rattle the tambourine and drums together,
    rattle the tambourine and drums, *hamesha.*
        Rabb ki howe sana.
        Sing the Lord's praises . . .

6   Play the flute so sweet and melodious,
    play the flute so sweet and melodious;
    clashing the cymbals and gongs together,
    clashing the cymbals together, *hamesha.*
        Rabb ki howe sana.
        Sing the Lord's praises . . .

7   Everybody clap hands together,
    everybody clap hands together;
    sing the Lord's praises for ever and ever,
    sing the Lord's praises for ever, *hamesha.*
        Rabb ki howe sana.
        Sing the Lord's praises . . .

126 SANNA

SOUTH AFRICA

Words: traditional
Music: unknown
arranged Geoff Weaver

Sanna is a shortened form of *Hosanna*. It is very effective to start this song quietly, as if in a distant procession, and then to get louder and more exuberant as the imaginary procession draws nearer.

127 SANTO, SANTO
Holy, holy

ARGENTINA

Words and music: unknown
arranged Geoff Weaver

Worshipfully ♩ = 84

San - to, san - to, san - to, mí co - ra - zón te a -
Ho - ly, ho - ly, ho - ly, my heart, my heart a -

- do - ra! Mi co - ra - zón te
- dores you! My heart is glad to

sabe de - cir: san - to eres Se - ñor.
say the_ words: you are ho - ly, Lord.

> This heart-felt love song may be sung in
> unison, in two parts, or in rich harmony.

Santo, santo, santo,
mi corazón te adora!
Mi corazón te sabe decir:
santo eres Señor.

Holy, holy, holy,
my heart, my heart adores you!
My heart is glad to say the words:
you are holy, Lord.

INSTRUMENTAL OBLIGATO

Oboe

Flute

Bb Clarinet

Simple part

128 SANTO, SANTO, SANTO
Holy, holy, holy is the Lord

EL SALVADOR

Words: unknown
English adaptation, Word & Music
Music: unknown
arranged Christopher Norton

San - to, san - to, san - to, san - to, san - to,
Ho - ly, ho - ly, ho - ly, ho - ly, ho - ly,

san - toes nues - tro Dios, Se - ñor de to - da la tie - rra, san - to,
ho - ly is our God; God, the Lord of earth and hea - ven, ho - ly

san - toes nues - tro Dios. San - to, san - to, san - to, san - to, san - to,
ho - ly is our God. Ho - ly, ho - ly, ho - ly, ho - ly, ho - ly,

> This extract from the *Missa Popular Salvadorena*, with its characteristic folk
> dance alternation of $\frac{6}{8}$ and $\frac{3}{4}$ time, needs a lively rhythmic accompaniment
> (percussion and guitars) and a radiant abandon on the part of the congregation.

129 SARANAM, SARANAM
Jesus, Saviour, Lord

PAKISTAN

Words: from Psalm 61
after D. T. Niles
Music: Punjabi melody
arranged Geoff Weaver

With feeling ♩ = 88

Sa - ra - nam, sa - ra - nam, sa - ra - nam,

Je - sus, Sav - iour, Lord, now to you I come, Sa - ra -

- nam, sa - ra-nam, sa - ra - nam; you my Rock, my re - fuge, my

hea - venly home, Sa - ra - nam, sa - ra-nam, sa - ra - nam.

A hymn much loved by Christians from the Indian subcontinent, based on words by
D. T. Niles and set to a Punjabi melody. 'Saranam' means 'refuge' or 'I take refuge'.

1 From the earth wher-ev-er I may be, out of des-pe-ra-tion and through
2 In your heart give me a hid-ing place, and be-neath your wings let me find

a - go - ny, I cry in help-less-ness— O
shel - tering grace; O let me see the sun-shine

ans - wer me, Sa - ra - nam, sa - ra-nam, sa - ra - nam.
of your face,

D.S.

3 Then with joy to you my vows I'll pay,
   and give thanks for all your mercy every day;
   I'll humbly follow in your perfect way,
   Saranam, saranam, saranam.
      Jesus, Saviour . . .

4 Glory to the Father and the Son,
   with the Holy Spirit ever Three-in-One;
   we'll sing in heaven praises here begun,
   Saranam, saranam, saranam.
      Jesus, Saviour . . .

130 SENHOR, TEM PIEDADE DE NÓS
O Lord, have mercy on us

KYRIE

Music: Jaci C. Maraschin
arranged David Peacock

Underlying this wonderful Brazilian setting of the Kyrie, are the rhythms of the dance. The melodic line should be smooth, the accompaniment much less so.

131 SENT BY THE LORD AM I

NICARAGUA

Words: from the oral tradition
translation Jorge Maldonodo
Music: traditional
arranged David Peacock

Confidently ♩ = 100

Capo 3(Dm)

Sent by the Lord am I; my hands are rea-dy now to make the earth the place in which the king-dom comes. Sent

HARMONY

by the Lord am I; my hands are rea-dy now to make the earth the place in which the king-dom comes. The

A song from the folk tradition of Nicaragua. The use of the minor key somehow adds strength and resolve to the commitment to Christ's mission.

Sent by the Lord am I;
my hands are ready now
to make the earth the place
in which the kingdom comes.
Sent by the Lord am I;
my hands are ready now
to make the earth the place
in which the kingdom comes.

The angels cannot change
a world of hurt and pain
into a world of love,
of justice and of peace.
The task is mine to do,
to set it really free.
Oh, help me to obey;
help me to do your will.

132 SHE DANCED AMID THE CITY LIGHTS

ERMITA

Words: from John 20:18 and 4:39–42
after Tom Maddela, paraphrased Rolando S. Timo
Music: Francisco F. Feliciano
arranged Geoff Weaver

Simply ♩ = 84

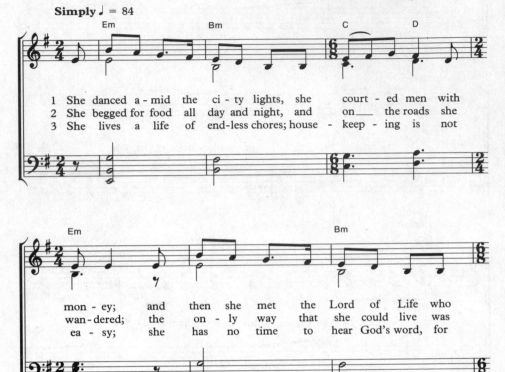

1 She danced a-mid the ci-ty lights, she court-ed men with
2 She begged for food all day and night, and on___ the roads she
3 She lives a life of end-less chores; house-keep-ing is not

mon-ey; and then she met the Lord of Life who
wan-dered; the on-ly way that she could live was
ea-sy; she has no time to hear God's word, for

of-fered her his mer-cy. This Mag-da-lene named
cha-ri-ty from oth-ers. And then she met the
she___ is al-ways bu-sy. But e-ven now, the

A moving Filipino song in which the lives of three women in the New Testament are related to the lives of so many women in the Philippines and throughout the world today. The melody, by one of the leading composers in the Philippines, is named after one of the notorious 'red light' areas of downtown Manila.

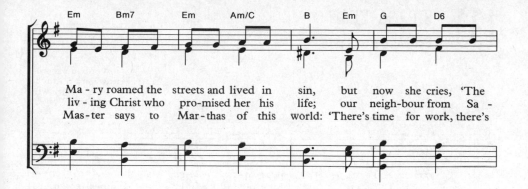

Ma - ry roamed the streets and lived in sin, but now she cries, 'The
liv - ing Christ who pro-mised her his life; our neigh-bour from Sa -
Mas-ter says to Mar-thas of this world: 'There's time for work, there's

Lord is ris - en: come with me and lis-ten!'
- mar - ia tells us, 'Christ is here to help you.'
time to lis - ten — be - hold your sis - ter Ma-ry.'

1 She danced amid the city lights, she courted men with money;
   and then she met the Lord of Life who offered her his mercy.
   This Magdalene named Mary roamed the streets and lived in sin,
   but now she cries, 'The Lord is risen: come with me and listen!'

2 She begged for food all day and night, and on the roads she wandered;
   the only way that she could live was charity from others.
   And then she met the living Christ who promised her his life;
   our neighbour from Samaria tells us, 'Christ is here to help you.'

3 She lives a life of endless chores; housekeeping is not easy;
   she has no time to hear God's word, for she is always busy.
   But even now, the Master says to Marthas of this world:
   'There's time for work, there's time to listen – behold your sister Mary.'

133 SIFASA YESU
Praise be to Jesus

EAST AFRICA

Words: unknown
translated Word & Music
Music: unknown
arranged Geoff Weaver

March-like ♩ = 116

Si - fa - sa Ye su, mwa-na-wa mun-gu, A - li - po -
Praise be to Je-sus! Sing of his glo-ry — heal-er and

-ku - a ha - pa du - ni - a - ni, Ki - la ma - ha - li a - li - po -
help-er — the Lord of love and grace. Here in the gos-pel we read the

-kwen-da, a - li - po - nya wo-te na vi - le - ma.
sto - ry Christ is our peace: to God be all the praise!

A very typical East African worship song, with its lively rhythms and its teaching about the power of Jesus. A rhythmic accompaniment is always effective.

Si - fa - sa Ye su, mwa-na - wa mun-gu, A - li - po -
Praise be to Je - sus! Sing of his glo - ry – heal - er and

- ku - a ha - pa du-ni - a - ni, Ki - la ma - ha - li a - li - po -
help-er – the Lord of love and grace. Here in the gos-pel we read the

- kwen-da, a - li - po - nya wo - te na vi - le - ma.
sto - ry Christ is our peace: to God be all the praise!

Sifasa Yesu,	Praise be to Jesus!
mwanawa mungu,	Sing of his glory –
Alipokua	healer and helper –
hapa duniani,	the Lord of love and grace.
Kila mahali	Here in the gospel
alipokwenda,	we read the story
aliponya	Christ is our peace:
wote na vilema.	to God be all the praise!

134 SING OF HIS VICTORY

EGYPT

Words: from Revelation 4 & 5
Word & Music
Music: unknown
arranged Geoff Weaver

Gently ♩. = 69

1 Sing of his vic-to-ry, tell of his sac-ri-fice:
worthy the Lamb of God who shall re-ceive our love!
Let ev-ery crea-ture bring true praise to wor-ship him —
hon-our and wis-dom and power for ev-er-more.

2 Je-sus, you died for us, pur-chased our li-ber-ty,
made us a priest-ly king-dom, fit to serve our God:
from all hu-ma-ni-ty, now to your glo-ry be
hon-our and wis-dom and power for ev-er-more!

The ancient Egyptian Coptic Church is rich in history and tradition. Its liturgy is elaborate and colourful, but there is also a place for simple songs from the heart, such as this item of praise. This is most effective as a solo.

135 SIYAHAMBA
We are marching

SOUTH AFRICA

Words: African origin
collected and edited by Anders Nyberg
English verses 2 and 3: Andrew Maries
Music: African melody scored by
Notman KB, Ljungsbro and Lars Parkman

An exuberant song of hope from South Africa which has become popular in recent years.
Experiment with variations in the harmony. It is hard to stand still while singing this song!

Joyfully ♩ = 120

OPTIONAL FURTHER VERSES

2 We are living in the love of God . . .

3 We are moving in the power of God . . .

136 SIZOHAMBA NAYE
We are on the Lord's road

SOUTH AFRICA

Words and music: unknown

Lively ♩ = 63

Capo 3(D)

1 Si - zo-ham-ba na - ye (wo)____
1 We are on_ the Lord's road, (wo)____

(wo)____ si - zo-ham-ba na - ye
(wo)____ we are on_ the Lord's road,

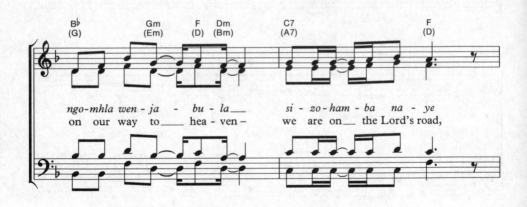

ngo-mhla wen - ja - bu - la____ si - zo-ham-ba na - ye
on our way to____ hea - ven- we are on_ the Lord's road,

ngo-mhla wen - ja - bu - la____ si - zo-ham-ba na - ye.
on our way to____ hea - ven- we are on_ the Lord's road.

> A lively song from South Africa. Try and feel the rhythms as exactly as possible.

1 *Sizohamba naye (wo) sizohamba naye*
  Sizohamba naye . . .
  ngomhla wenjabula
  sizohamba naye
  ngomhla wenjabula
  sizohamba naye.

2 *Sizohalalisa (wo) sizohalalisa*
  sizohalalisa . . .
  ngomhla wenjabula
  sizohalalisa naye
  ngomhla wenjabula
  sizohalalisa naye.

3 *Sizohlabelela (wo) sizohlabelela*
  sizohlabelela . . .
  ngomhla wenjabula
  sizohlabelela naye
  ngomhla wenjabula
  sizohlabelela naye.

1 We are on the Lord's road,
   we are on the Lord's road,
we are on the Lord's road,
   we are on the Lord's road,
on our way to heaven –
we are on the Lord's road,
on our way to heaven –
we are on the Lord's road.

2 We shall sing the Lord's praise,
   we shall sing the Lord's praise,
we shall sing the Lord's praise,
   we shall sing the Lord's praise,
on our way to heaven –
we shall sing the Lord's praise,
on our way to heaven –
we shall sing the Lord's praise.

3 We shall live the Lord's word,
   we shall live the Lord's word,
we shall live the Lord's word,
   we shall live the Lord's word,
on our way to heaven –
we shall live the Lord's word,
on our way to heaven –
we shall live the Lord's word.

4 Hallelujah, amen,
   hallelujah, amen,
hallelujah, amen,
   hallelujah, amen,
on our way to heaven –
hallelujah, amen,
on our way to heaven –
hallelujah, amen.

137 TAMA NGAKAU
Lord of love

Words: from Romans 3:21–26
traditional Maori, paraphrased Michael Perry
Music: Maori traditional melody
arranged Geoff Weaver

With expression ♩ = 50

1 Ta - ma nga - kau ma - ri - e, ta - ma
1 Lord of love, you come to bless all who

a T'a - tu - a,____ te - nei to - nu
will by faith con - fess____ Je - sus, God's own

ma - tou, a - ro - hai - na mai.
right - eous - ness to the world made known.

A simple prayer, based on a traditional Maori melody, most effective when sung unaccompanied.

- *tou,*   *a* - *ro* - *hai* - *na*   *mai.*
- ness   to   the   world   made   known.

1 *Tama ngakau marie,*
   tama a T'atua,
   tenei tonu matou,
   arohaina mai.

2 *Murua ra nga hara:*
   wete kina mai,
   enei here kino,
   whakararu nei.

3 *Homai he aroha*
   mou i mate nei
   tenei ra, e lhu
   takina e koe.

1 Lord of love, you come to bless
   all who will by faith confess
   Jesus, God's own righteousness
   to the world made known.

2 Bruised on Calvary's weary road,
   bowed beneath the curse of God,
   shedding the atoning blood
   sacrifice is done.

3 By the arms you open wide,
   by your wounded hands and side,
   Jesus, we are justified,
   saved by grace alone!

138

TATA POKELELA
Everything is yours, Lord

ZAMBIA

Words: from 1 Chronicles 29, unknown
English: Word & Music
Music: unknown
arranged Geoff Weaver

Joyfully ♩ = 132

LEADER

Ta - ta po - ke - le - la   If - ya - bu - pe fye - su,
Ev - ery-thing is yours,   Lord;   ev - ery-thing comes from   you:

If - yo twa - mi pe - la_____ le - lo.
all   we   have   we   of - fer_____ to   you.

An offertory song, in leader-response format. Improvised percussion accompaniment will help to give something of the flavour of the offertory, which in African worship is so often an exuberant (and extended!) experience.

Po - ke - le - le - ni_____ ta - ta,_____
Ac - cept our love, Lord,_____ we pray;_____

Po - ke - le - le - ni_____ le - lo.
re - ceive our gifts, Lord,_____ to - day.

139 TATANACA, MAMANACA, SARANTAÑANI
Men and women, let us walk

BOLIVIA

Words and music: Zoilo Yanapa
arranged Christopher Norton

1 Ta - ta - na - ca, ma - ma - na - ca, Sa - ran - ta - ña - ni!
(2) Igle - sia na - ca - sa - ja ma - ya-ghasi-ña - ni,
1 Men and wo-men, let us walk, and let's walk to - ge-ther;
(2) Church be one strong bo - dy, walk-ing to - ge-ther;

Ta - ta - na - ca, ma - ma - na - ca, Sa - ran - ta - ña - ni! Way - na -
ta - ke Igle - sia na - ca - sa - ja ma - ya-ghasi-ña - ni. Ma - ya -
men and wo-men, let us walk, and let's walk to - ge-ther. Bro-thers,
let the Church be one strong bo - dy, walk-ing to - ge-ther. Ev - ery

- na - ka, ta - wa - co - na - ka, sayt' a - si - ña - ni. Way - na -
- qui, ta - ke - ni, Sa - ran - ta - ña - ni. Ma - ya -
sis - ters, child - ren and youth, let's all move to - ge - ther; bro-thers,
mem - ber touched by each o - ther, keep-ing to - ge - ther; ev - ery

---

This dance-song comes from the Aymara people of Bolivia. With such vitality in their worship,
it is not surprising that they are part of the fastest growing church in their country.

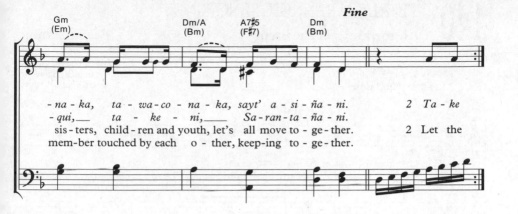

Fine

Gm (Em) Dm/A (Bm) A7#5 (F#7) Dm (Bm)

-na - ka, ta - wa - co - na - ka, sayt' a - si - ña - ni.   2 Ta - ke
-qui,___ ta - ke - ni,___ Sa - ran - ta - ña - ni.   2 Let the
sis - ters, child - ren and youth, let's all move to - ge - ther.
mem - ber touched by each o - ther, keep - ing to - ge - ther.

1   *Tatanaca, mamanaca, Sarantañani!*
    Tatanaca, mamanaca, Sarantañani!
    Waynanaka, tawaconaka, sayt' asiñani.
    Waynanaka, tawaconaka, sayt' asiñani.

2   *Take Iglesia nacasaja mayaghasiñani,*
    take Iglesia nacasaja mayaghasiñani.
    Mayaqui, takeni, Sarantañani.
    Mayaqui, takeni, Sarantañani.

1   Men and women, let us walk,
    and let's walk together;
  men and women, let us walk,
    and let's walk together.
  Brothers, sisters, children and youth,
    let's all move together;
  brothers, sisters, children and youth,
    let's all move together.

2   Let the Church be one strong body,
    walking together;
  let the Church be one strong body,
    walking together.
  Every member touched by each other,
    keeping together;
  every member touched by each other,
    keeping together.

140 TE ALABARÁN, OH SEÑOR
All the kings of the earth

EL SALVADOR

Words: from Psalm 138
Music: from El Salvador
arranged Geoff Weaver

Lively ♩ = 132
DESCANT 2nd time
Capo 3(D)

Te a-la-ba - rán, oh Se - ñor to - dos los re - yes
All the kings of the earth shall praise you, Lord,___

to-dos los re-yes de la tie - rra por-que hon-o - í - do los di - chos de tu
all__ the kings of the earth;__ for they have heard the won-ders of your

bo - ca y can - ta - rán de los ca-mi-nos del Se - ñor. Te a-la-ba-
mouth, and they shall sing_ of the ways of the Lord. All the

The people of El Salvador have a long history of suffering and oppression at the hands of the powerful and the wealthy. This joyful psalm of praise is a song of hope and trust in the Lord who 'regards the lowly'. Ideally it should be sung with guitar and light rhythmic accompaniment.

141 TE ALABARÉ
I'll trust you, Lord

ARGENTINA

Words and music: Claudio Tischier
English: Word & Music
music arranged David Peacock

Unhurried ♩ = 72

1 *Te a-la-ba-ré,____ no im-por-ta*
1 I'll trust you, Lord =____ your love to

co-mo es-té;____ te a-la-ba-ré,____ en ti yo
me is real; I'll trust you, Lord,____ no mat-ter

ten-go fe.____ Aun-que los o - jos de-jen de__ bri-llar,
how I feel – and when I weep a-lone I'll trust you, Lord;

aun-que la voz__ se a - pa - gue y no quie-ra__ can-tar;
yes, e - ven when my hope is gone I'll trust you, Lord.

A song, collected by Baptist Christians in Argentina, which
encourages us to live for God, even in difficult circumstances.

aun - que los o - jos de - jen de __ bri - llar, __ aun-que la voz _ se a -
And when I weep a-lone I'll trust you, Lord; yes, e-ven when my

1.2.
3.

- pa - gue y no quie-ra __ can - tar. 2 Te ser - vi - ré __ - dar.
hope is gone I'll trust you, Lord. 2 I'll serve you, Lord–Lord.

2 Te serviré, no importa como esté;
   te serviré, en tí yo tengo fe.
   Aunque el dolor comience a preguntar
   aunque la luz se apague y no quiera brillar;
   aunque el dolor comience a preguntar
   aunque la luz se apague y no quiera brillar.

3 Me alegraré en Cristo, mi Señor;
   me alegraré en tí, mi Salvador.
   Si alguna vez sin fuerza he de quedar
   tú eres mi fortaleza y tú me harás andar;
   si alguna vez sin fuerza he de quedar
   tú eres mi fortaleza y tú me harás andar.

2 I'll serve you, Lord – because your love is true,
   I'll serve you, Lord, and live my life for you;
   and though my faith is weak
       I'll serve you, Lord;
   yes, in your Spirit's power I'll speak,
       and serve you, Lord.
   And though my faith . . .

3 I'll praise you, Lord, for you are Christ my king,
   I'll praise you, Lord, and you alone I'll sing;
   and so through all my days
       I'll praise you, Lord;
   yes, I will give you all the praise –
       I'll praise you, Lord.
   And so through . . .

142 TE ALABARÉ, OH JEHOVÁ

How beautiful is our Saviour

CHILE

Words: unknown
paraphrased Word & Music
Music: unknown
arranged David Peacock

Steadily ♩ = 100

Te a - la-ba-ré, oh Jeh-o-vá, con to-do mi co-ra-zón, con
How beau-ti-ful is our Sav - iour, won-der-ful is his mer - cy,

to-do mi co-ra-zón. Te a - la - ba-ré, oh Jeh-o-vá.
glo-ri-ous is his good - ness: praise him and re-joice!

Con - ta - ré to-das tus ma - ra-vill-as,
Je - sus reigns – let the whole world bring trib-ute,

to-das tus ma - ra-vill-as. Te a - la - ba-ré, oh Jeh-o-vá. Me a -
ce-le-brate with thanks-giv-ing and bow be-fore his throne! For

A lively song set to a typically repetitive Chilean melody.

143 TE AMO
I love you

ARGENTINA

Words and music: unknown
arranged David Peacock

Unhurried ♩ = 80

Te a - mo, te a - mo es
I love you, I love you – the

to - do lo que pue - do___ de - cir._____ Te a -
earth and hea - ven show forth__ your ways._____ I

- do - ro, te a - do - ro, to - do mi ser con - fí - a en
love you, I love you; with all my heart I sing out your

ti._____ Yo te a - ma - ré_____ y te a -
praise._____ I praise you, O Lord,___ yes, I

An expressive worship song which is sung throughout Latin America.

Te amo, te amo
es todo lo que puedo decir.
Te adoro, te adoro,
todo mi ser confía en ti.

Yo te amaré y te adoraré
no importa lo que pueda venir.
En ti Señor siempre confiaré
y te amaré hasta el fin.

I love you, I love you –
the earth and heaven show forth your ways.
I love you, I love you;
with all my heart I sing out your praise.

I praise you, O Lord, yes, I praise you, O Lord,
for every gift and true joy you send;
I love you, O Lord, yes, I love you, Lord,
and I will love you to the end.

144 TE EXALTAMOS
We exalt you, mighty Lord

MEXICO

From Psalm 141
Words and music: Marcos Witt
English: Word & Music
arranged David Peacock

Lively ♩ = 130

Te e - xal - ta - mos so-bre un tro - no de a - la - ban - za,
We ex - alt___ you, might - y Lord, en - throned in glo - ry;

te e - xal - ta - mos, oh Se - ñor.
we ex - alt___ you, might - y Lord!

Nues - tras a - la - ban - zas su - bi - rán de - lan - te
As the even - ing sac - ri - fi - ces___ rise, our prais - es

de tu tro - no, oh Se - ñor. O -
greet the Lord___ of ma - jes - ty — to

> One of the most popular worship songs from Marcos Witt which has travelled
> beyond Mexico. A steady back-beat is essential to maintain rhythmic vitality.

145 TERI ARADHANA KARU
Lord, in your mercy, remember me

INDIA

Words: after the Indian song
from Psalm 25, Word & Music
Music: unknown
arranged Geoff Weaver

Te – ri a – ra – dha – na_____ ka – ru
Lord, in your mer – cy, re – mem – ber me,

Te – ri a – ra – dha – na_____ ka – ru
Lord, in your mer – cy, re – mem – ber me;

Pa – pa – ksha – ma ker jee – van_____ de – dey
show me your ways, Lord, guide me in your truth and teach me, Lord:

This is only the refrain of a much longer song originally in Hindi, and sung as a morning prayer. Its character is perhaps best expressed by a solo female voice, as the arranger first heard it hauntingly sung by a young Indian woman.

Teri aradhana karu
Teri aradhana karu
Papakshama ker jeevan dedey
dayaki yachana karu.

Teri aradhana karu.
Teri aradhana karu.

Lord, in your mercy, remember me,
Lord, in your mercy, remember me;
show me your ways, Lord,
guide me in your truth and teach me, Lord:
you are my God, my king, my saviour.

Lord, in your mercy, remember me.
Lord, in your mercy, remember me.

146 TERI BAR KAT HAM PAR HO

On creation let your blessing fall

PAKISTAN

Words: unknown
English: Alison Blenkinsop
Music: unknown
arranged Geoff Weaver

Strongly rhythmic ♩ = 120

Te - ri bar (a) kat (a) ham par (a) ho.___

On cre - a - tion let your bless - ing___ fall:

Prab-hu, Yi - su, te - ri jai___ jai___ ho.

Last time **to Coda** ⊕

We praise you, Je - sus,___ Lord___ of___ all.

A typically languid Indian melody, characterized by a rather ambivalent tonality. Imaginative contrasts of 'solo' and 'full' will add to the effectiveness of this song of praise to the Creator.

na - ture's beau - ty___ has us in thrall,
rush - ing stream and___ great wa - ter - fall,___
there we see___ how___ you feed us all,___
your___ sac - ri - fice___ for great and small,

D.S.

na - ture's beau - ty___ has us in thrall.
rush - ing stream and___ great wa - ter - fall.___
there we see___ how___ you feed us all.___
your___ sac - ri - fice___ for great and small.

✛ *CODA*

We praise you, Je - sus,___ Lord of___ all. You are

Lord___ of___ all; you are Lord___ of___ all.

147 THE DEER LONGS

CARIBBEAN

Words: from Psalm 42
after George Mulrain, Word & Music
Music: Caribbean
arranged David Peacock

Strongly rhythmic ♩ = 72

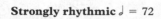

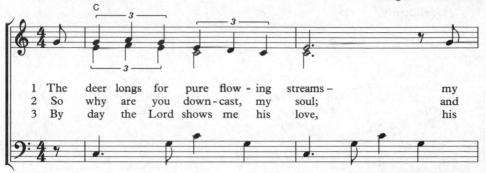

1 The deer longs for pure flow-ing streams — my
2 So why are you down-cast, my soul; and
3 By day the Lord shows me his love, his

thirs-ty soul longs for the Lord: I have been weep-ing all day and all
why are you cry-ing a-lone? You must re-mem-ber to put all your
bless-ings sur-round me at night: so I will tell out his faith-ful-ness,

night, for they say, 'Tell us, when will your God keep his word?'
trust in your God, and to praise him for what he has done.
sing of his grace, and, re-joic-ing, I'll walk in his light!

George Mulrain, a pastor and teacher from the Caribbean, set the words of the psalmist to this traditional melody. Rhythmic freedom is the essence here, noting the contrast of the ♩ ♩ ♩ with the rhythm of the ostinato.

148 THE LORD IS MY LIGHT

CZECHOSLOVAKIA

Words: from Psalm 27
paraphrased John L. Bell
Music: Czech hymn tune
arranged Geoff Weaver

Confidently ♩ = 138

1 The Lord is my light, my light and
2 Should e - vil powers ad - vance, should arm - ies
3 One thing I ask the Lord. This on - ly
4 Pre - served by God from harm, se - cure in

my sal - va - tion. With God pro - tect - ing me
try to kill, let them sur - round me and
I de - sire: al - ways in wor - ship to
him a - lone, I will re - joice in the

from ev - ery dan - ger, whom shall I fear?
let them at - tack me, I'll still trust God.
gaze at God's good - ness and seek his aid.
face of af - flic - tion and sing God's song.

A setting of Psalm 27 based on a 17th century Czech hymn tune and sung, amongst others, by the Evangelical Church of the Czech Brethren. The minor mode gives it a strength and seriousness of purpose. It can be sung either in parts or in unison with keyboard accompaniment.

149 THE MOST EXCELLENCY IS JESUS

NIGERIA

Words: unknown
collected Geoff Weaver
Music: unknown
arranged Geoff Weaver

Free rhythms ♩. = 66

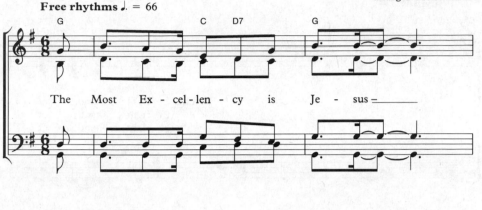

The Most Ex - cel - len - cy is Je - sus __

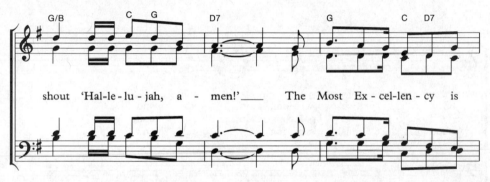

shout 'Hal - le - lu - jah, a - men!' __ The Most Ex - cel - len - cy is

Je - sus __ shout 'Hal - le - lu - jah, a - men!' __

The arranger had some difficulty in notating this song in Kano Cathedral, Nigeria, largely due to the complex, intuitive rhythms. Feel them, rather than trying to count them!

150 THE RIGHT HAND OF GOD

CARIBBEAN

Words: after Patrick Prescord
Word & Music
Music: Noel Dexter
arranged Christopher Norton

1 The right hand of
(2) right hand of
(3) right hand of

God is writ-ing in our land,
God is point-ing in our land,
God is strik-ing in our land,

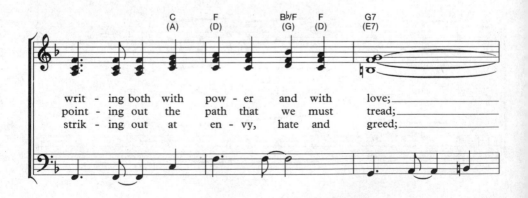

writ - ing both with pow - er and with love;
point - ing out the path that we must tread;
strik - ing out at en - vy, hate and greed;

> A song of judgment, justice and mercy from the Caribbean.
> It is very important to feel the rhythmic freedom here.

Words: in this version Word & Music / Jubilee Hymns

our con-flicts and — our fears, our
so cloud-ed is —— the way, so
our self - ish - ness — and lust, our

tri-umphs and — our tears, are re - cord-ed by — the
ea - si - ly — we stray, but we're guid-ed by — the
pride, and deeds un - just are con - demned by — the

right hand of God.
right hand of God.
right hand of God.

2 The
3 The
4 The

4   The right hand of God is healing in our land,
    healing broken bodies, minds and souls;
        so when we bow in prayer,
        the love of Christ is there
    and we're healed by the right hand of God.

5   The right hand of God is planting in our land,
    planting seeds of freedom, hope and love.
        In this and every place
        all we who live by grace
    can be one with the right hand of God.

151 THUMA MINA
Send me, Lord

SOUTH AFRICA

Words: African origin,
collected and edited by Anders Nyberg
Music: African melody scored by Notman KB,
Ljungsbro and Lars Parkman

Worshipfully ♩ = 100

LEADER
Thu - ma mi - na,
Send me,_ Lord:

ALL
Thu - ma mi - na thu - ma mi - na thu - ma
Send me, Je-sus, send me, Je - sus, send me,

thu - ma mi - na
send me,_ Lord.

mi - na, so - man - dla.
Je - sus, send me, Lord.

Thu - ma - dla.
Send me, Lord.

LEADER	*Thuma mina,*	
ALL	*thuma mina*	
	thuma mina	
	thuma mina,	
	somandla.	

1 LEADER Send me, Lord:
  ALL Send me, Jesus,
    send me, Jesus,
    send me, Jesus,
    send me, Lord.

2 LEADER Lead me, Lord:
  ALL Lead me, Jesus . . .

3 LEADER Fill me, Lord:
  ALL Fill me, Jesus . . .

Both this and the following setting of the text come from the rich South
African tradition of sacred song which is noted for its harmonies and for its
strength and dignity. Sing these songs unaccompanied and use them in a
variety of ways, e.g. after intercessions, after a talk, at the end of the service.

152 THUMA MINA
Send me, Jesus

Words and music:
transcribed from the singing of Lulu Dumazweni
arranged John L. Bell

As quickly as the mood requires

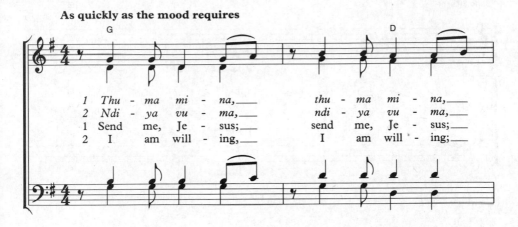

1 *Thuma mina, thuma mina,*
  thuma mina, Nkosi yam.

2 *Ndiya vuma, ndiya vuma,*
  ndiya vuma, Nkosi yam.

1 Send me, Jesus; send me, Jesus;
  send me, Jesus; send me, Lord.

2 I am willing, I am willing;
  I am willing, willing, Lord.

153 TOUT EST FAIT POUR LA GLOIRE DE DIEU
All is made for the glory of God

CAMEROON

Words and music: Abel Nkuinji
arranged Geoff Weaver

1 Tout est fait pour la gloi - re de Dieu. A -
1 All is made for the glo - ry of God. A -

- men, (A - men) a - men! Tout est fait pour la
- men, (A - men) a - men! All is made for the

SOLO Al - le - lu - ia___
Al - le - lu - ia___

gloi - re de Dieu. A - men, (A - men) a - men, a - men,_ a -
glo - ry of God. A - men, (A - men) a - men, a - men, a -

> A lively rhythmic song from French-speaking West Africa. It can
> be extended indefinitely, as is the practice in Africa, by naming
> other subjects and creatures which exist for God's glory.

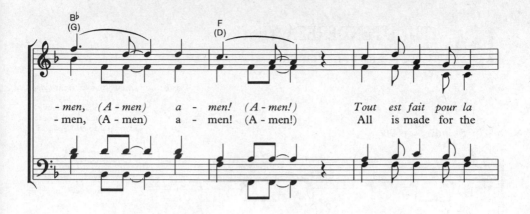

-men, (A-men) a - men! (A-men!) Tout est fait pour la
-men, (A-men) a - men! (A-men!) All is made for the

gloi - re de Dieu. A - men, (A - men) a - men!
glo - ry of God. A - men, (A - men) a - men!

1 Tout est fait pour la gloire de Dieu.
   Amen, amen!
   Tout est fait pour la gloire de Dieu.
   Amen, amen, amen, amen, amen!
   Tout est fait pour la gloire de Dieu.
   Amen, amen!

2 La vie c'est pour la gloire de Dieu ...

3 Le culte est pour la gloire de Dieu ...

1 All is made for the glory of God.
   Amen, amen!
   All is made for the glory of God.
   Amen, amen, amen, amen, amen!
   All is made for the glory of God.
   Amen, amen!

2 Living is for the glory of God ...

3 Worship is for the glory of God ...

154 TUKUTENDEREZA YESU
Glory, glory, hallelujah

EAST AFRICA

Words: from the Luganda, unknown
translated L. Rouse
Music: African, unknown
English: D. Boole
arranged David Peacock

Tu - ku - ten - de - re - za Ye - su, Ye - su

Omwa - na gw'en - di - ga; o - mu - sai - gwo gu - na -

- zi - za - n - kwe - ba - za, O - mu - lo - ko - zi.

The great song of the East African Revival, with all its resonances of 'walking in the light' and the transformation of so many lives. The Luganda version is based on an existing English hymn. The English text cannot be sung to the Luganda adaptation of the music.

Glo - ry, glo - ry, hal - le - lu - jah! Glo - ry,

glo - ry to the Lamb! Oh, the cleans - ing blood has

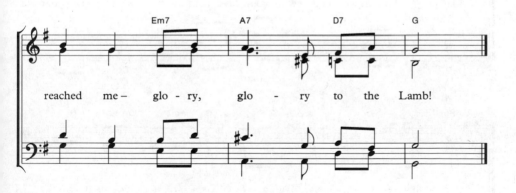

reached me – glo - ry, glo - ry to the Lamb!

Tukutendereza Yesu,
Yesu Omwana gw'endiga;
omusaigwo gunaziza –
nkwebaza, Omulokozi.

Glory, glory, hallelujah!
Glory, glory to the Lamb!
Oh, the cleansing blood has reached me –
glory, glory to the Lamb!

155 TULE KANSSANI
Living Lord

FINLAND

Words and music: Hilga Haahti
English: Word & Music
arranged Geoff Weaver

With simplicity ♩ = 84

1 Tu - le kans - sa - ni, Her - ra Jee - sus, tu - le, siu - naa__ päl - vän
2 Tu - le as - ke - le as - ke - lee - lta mi - nun kans - sa - ni kul - ke -
1 Liv - ing Lord, turn your face to - wards me, hear the prayer that I bring to -
2 Liv - ing Lord, turn your heart to - wards me, bless the song that I sing to -

työ. Tu - le il - loin ja aa - muln var - hain. Tu - le
- maan. Su - a il - man en saa - ta ol - la, py - sy
- day; fill my heart with your love each morn - ing, come and
- day; fill my mind with your love each eve - ning, give your

vie - lä, kun jou - tuu yö, tu - le vie - lä, kun jou - tuu yö.
luo - na - ni ai - ni - aan, py - sy luo - na - ni ai - ni - aan.
walk with me all the way, come and walk with me all the way.
peace to my heart, I pray, give your peace to my heart, I pray.

A haunting song, rather folk-like in character, much loved by Finnish Christians.

156 TUYO ES EL REINO
Yours is the kingdom

ARGENTINA

Words: from the Lord's Prayer
Music: Pablo D. Sosa
arranged Geoff Weaver

The composer Pablo Sosa has written much music for worship with an authentically Latin American flavour. Here is the certainty of God's Kingdom allied to the vitality of the dance. It should be sung with vigour, a growing sense of excitement and a guitar and percussion accompaniment.

157

TY WYZWOLILES NAS (ABBA OJCZE)
Brothers and sisters

POLAND

Words: J. Góra
English: Word & Music
Music: J. Sykulski
arranged Geoff Weaver

Lively with majesty ♩ = 112

1 Ty wyz - wo - li - les nas, Pa - nie
2 Bo Kos - ci - ol jak drz - e - wo zyc - ia w wie -
1 Bro - thers and sis - ters, of God we sing, the
2 Bro - thers and sis - ters, of Christ we sing, the

z kaj - dan i sa - mych sie - bie, a Chrys - tus sta - jac sie
- czno - sci za - pu - szcza kor - ze - nie prze - ni - ka nas - za cod -
Fa - ther who has made us all. O God, we give you the
Sav - iour who re - deemed us all. O God, we give you the

bra - tem na - uczyl nas wo - lac do Cie - bie:
- zien - nosc i po - ka - zu - je nam Cie - bie.
glo - ry, we give you the praise and the glo - ry:
glo - ry, we give you the praise and the glo - ry:

This song, which has become popular in ecumenical gatherings, breathes the joy in new-found freedom, in all its aspects, which Christians from Eastern Europe understand well. It should be strongly rhythmic, and has something of the character of a march. When using the English version, 'Abba Ojcze' (pronounced 'Oi-chay') may be substituted at the end of each verse.

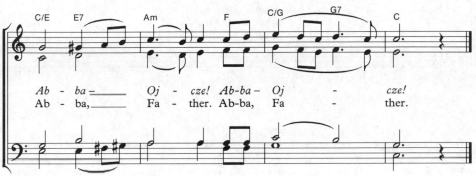

1　*Ty wyzwoliles nas, Panie*
　z kajdan i samych siebie,
　a Chrystus stajac sie bratem
　nauczyl nas wolac do Ciebie:
　　Abba – Ojcze! Abba – Ojcze!
　　Abba – Ojcze! Abba – Ojcze!

1　Brothers and sisters, of God we sing,
　the Father who has made us all.
　O God, we give you the glory,
　we give you the praise and the glory:
　　Abba, Father. Abba, Father.
　　Abba, Father. Abba, Father.

2　*Bo Kosciol jak drzewo zycia*
　w wiecznosci zapuszcza korzenie
　przenika nasza codziennosc
　i pokazuje nam Ciebie.
　　Abba – Ojcze . . .

2　Brothers and sisters, of Christ we sing,
　the Saviour who redeemed us all.
　O God, we give you the glory,
　we give you the praise and the glory:
　　Abba, Father . . .

3　*Bog hojnym Dawca jest zycia*
　On wyswobodzil nas z smierci
　i przygarniajac do siebie
　uczynil swoimi dziecmi.
　　Abba – Ojcze . . .

3　Brothers and sisters, of power we sing,
　the Spirit who empowers us all.
　O God, we give you the glory,
　we give you the praise and the glory:
　　Abba, Father . . .

4　*Wszyscy jestesmy bracmi*
　jestesmy jedna rodzina.
　Tej prawdy nic juz nie zacmi
　i teraz jest jej godzina.
　　Abba – Ojcze . . .

4　Brothers and sisters, to God we sing,
　to Father, Son and Spirit – all.
　O God, we give you the glory,
　we give you the praise and the glory:
　　Abba, Father . . .

158 UM POUCO ALÉM DO PRESENTE
No sorrow, no mourning, no crying

BRAZIL

Words and music: unknown
English: From Revelation 20–22
Michael Perry
arranged David Peacock

Dance-like ♩ = 96

1 Um   pou - co a - lém do pre - sen - te, a -
    (2) -ão de es - pe - ran - ça se   a - bre, pre -
1 No   sor - row, no mourn - ing, no   cry - ing, no
    (2) bright is the light of God's   ci - ty, how

- le - gre o fu - tu - ro a - nun - cia a   fu - ga das som - bras da
-nún - ci - o da flor que se   faz. Pro - mes - sa da tu - a pre -
hat - red, no hurt and no ly - ing: but free - dom and love and sal -
sure is his mer - cy and pi - ty! The dark - ness will con - quer it

mor - te, a   luz de um bem no - vo di - a.
-sen - ça que   vi - da ab - un - dan - te nos   traz.
- va - tion, and peace for each tribe and each na - tion:
ne - ver, for God is our glo - ry for ev - er.

> A joyful expectant song of the Kingdom, with all the rhythmic vitality that we would expect from the land of the Carnival. Guitars and tambourines seem a 'must' here!

1 Um pouco além do presente,
   alegre, o futuro anuncia
   a fuga das sombras da morte,
   a luz de um bem novo dia.
       Venha Leu Reino, Senhor.
       A festa da vida recria.
       A nossa espera e ardor
       transforma em plen alegria.
       Aiê – eia – aiê – aê – aê.

2 Botâo de esperança se abre,
   prenûncio da flor que se faz.
   Promessa da tua presença
   que vida abundante nos traz.
       Venha Leu Reino . . .

3 Saudade da terra sem males,
   do Eden de plumas e flores,
   da paz e justiça irmanadas,
   num mundo sem odio nem dores.
       Venha Leu Reino . . .

4 Saudades de um mundo sem guerras,
   anelos de paz e inocência:
   de corpos e maos que se encontram,
   sem armas, sem mortes, violência.
       Venha Leu Reino . . .

5 Saudades de um mundo sem donos:
   ausência de fortes e fracos,
   derrota de todo o sistema
   que cria palãcios, barracos.
       Venha Leu Reino . . .

6 Jã temos preciosa semente,
   penhor do teu Reino, agora.
   Futuro ilumina o presente,
   tu vens e virãs sem demora.
       Venha Leu Reino . . .

1 No sorrow, no mourning, no crying,
   no hatred, no hurt and no lying:
   but freedom and love and salvation,
   and peace for each tribe and each nation:
       Raise up your kingdom, O Lord,
       bring joy to the end of our story;
       then Jesus, true to your word –
       come, reign in your power and your glory;
       then Jesus, true to your word –
       come, reign in your power and your glory!
       Alleluia, alleluia, amen!

2 How bright is the light of God's city,
   how sure is his mercy and pity!
   The darkness will conquer it never,
   for God is our glory for ever.
       Raise up your kingdom . . .

3 Such rivers in heaven are flowing,
   such trees by the waters are growing!
   The leaves of the trees are for healing,
   God's love for the nations revealing.
       Raise up your kingdom . . .

4 What wonder and beauty descending,
   what songs and what laughter are blending!
   God's people, whose sins are forgiven –
   the Bride of the Lamb – come from heaven.
       Raise up your kingdom . . .

5 All-just is our God, and all-knowing –
   all-wise to our reaping and sowing:
   the judge of our love or defying,
   the giver of living or dying!
       Raise up your kingdom . . .

6 So deep is our thirst and our yearning,
   so great is the hope in us burning:
   we sing to our heavenly Father,
   'Send Jesus. Lord, come – maranatha!'
       Raise up your kingdom . . .

159 VEM, JESUS NOSSA ESPERANÇA
Come to be our hope, Lord Jesus

BRAZIL

Words: Jorge Rodríguez
Jaci C. Maraschin
Music: Marcilide de Oliveira Filko
arranged Christopher Norton

Jaci Maraschin is one of Brazil's foremost Church composers. For him the dance finds its place in worship reflecting hope, while the flattened third portrays the pain of oppression. A light rhythmic accompaniment helps to bring out the dance-like character here.

1 *Vem, Jesus nossa esperança*
   nossas vidas libertar.
   Vem, nascer em nós, criança
   vem o teu poder nos dar.
   Vem, liberta os prisioneiros
   da injustiça e da aflição;
   vem, reúne os brasi leiros
   em amor e em compreensão.

2 *Vem tecer um mundo novo*
   nos caminhos de verdade;
   para que, afinal, o povo
   viva em plena liberdade.
   Vem, Jesus, abre o futuro
   do teu reino de alegria.
   Vem, derruba o imenso muro
   que separa a noite e o dia.

1 Come to be our hope, Lord Jesus,
   come to set our people free;
   from oppression come, release us,
   turn defeat to victory!
   Come, release from every prison
   · those who suffer in our land:
   in your love we find the reason
   still to live and understand.

2 Come to build your new creation
   through the road of servanthood;
   give new life to every nation,
   changing evil into good.
   Come and open our tomorrow
   for a kingdom now so near;
   take away all human sorrow –
   give us hope in place of fear.

160 WA WA WA EMIMIMO
Come, O Holy Spirit, come

NIGERIA

Words and music: unknown
arranged Geoff Weaver

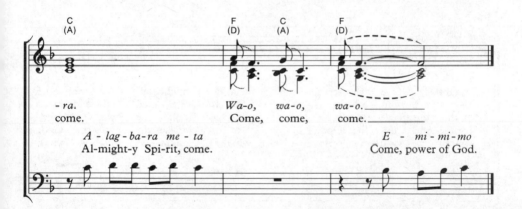

Wa wa wa Emimimo.
Wa wa wa Alagbara.
Wao, wao, wao.

Come, O Holy Spirit, come.
Come, Almighty Spirit, come.
Come, come, come.

First 3 times: sing at slow tempo ♩ = 88: 1. top line only (with tenor response); 2. add lower alto; 3. add guitar (first beat of every bar only); 4th time onwards sing faster at ♩ = 120. Add the middle part then percussion and more rhythmic guitar.

This Yoruba invocation of the Holy Spirit is very effective when sung slowly and quietly, gradually introducing voices and instruments on each repetition as indicated. A change of tempo with drums and clapping provides an exciting conclusion, always greeted with enthusiasm by Africans.

161 WHAT A MIGHTY GOD WE SERVE

SOUTH AFRICA

Words: unknown
Music: Zulu working song
arranged Peter Sandwell

With strength and joy ♩ = 140

1 What a might - y God we serve,___ what a
2 He cre - a - ted you and me,___ he cre -
3 He has all the power to save,___ he has
4 Let us praise the liv - ing God,___ let us
5 What a might - y God we serve,___ what a

might - y God we serve,___ what a might - y God we serve,
- a - ted you and me,___ he cre - a - ted you and me,
all the power to save,___ he has all the power to save,
praise the liv - ing God,___ let us praise the liv - ing God,
might - y God we serve,___ what a might - y God we serve,

___ what___ a might - y God we serve.___
___ he___ cre - a - ted you and me.___
___ he___ has all the power to save.___
___ let___ us praise the liv - ing God.___
___ what___ a might - y God we serve.___

A strong Zulu song of affirmation from South Africa.

162 WHOEVER LIVES BESIDE THE LORD

SCOTLAND

Words: from Psalm 91
John L. Bell
Music: Gaelic melody 'Teann a nall'
arranged John L. Bell

Gently ♩ = 88

1 Who-ev-er lives be-side the Lord, shelter-ing
2 From un-seen dan-ger and dis-ease God will
3 You will not dread what dark-ness brings— hid-den

in th'Al-might-y's shade, shall say, 'My God, in
keep you safe_ and sure; be-neath his wings a
dan-ger, dead-ly plague; nor will you fear, in

you I trust, my safe-ty, my de-fend-er.'
place you'll find, a re-fuge from all dan-ger.
day-light hours, the e-vil that sur-rounds__ you.

4 A thousand may die at your side,
thousands more fall close at hand;
but with God's truth for strength and shield,
no threat will ever touch you.

5 God says, 'I'll save from every harm
those who know and love my name.
In trouble I will honour them
and show them my salvation.'

From the *Psalms of Patience, Protest and Praise* collection

> A good match of a traditional Scottish melody and words from Psalm 91.
> This is best sung unaccompanied in harmony.

163 WHAT WONDROUS LOVE IS THIS

Words and music: American folk hymn
arranged David Peacock

Simply ♩ = 80

1 What wond-rous love is this, O my soul, O my
(2) God and to the Lamb, I will sing, I will
(3) when from death I'm free, I'll sing on, I'll sing

soul! What wond-rous love is this, O my soul! What
sing; to God and to the Lamb, I will sing. To
on, and when from death I'm free, I'll sing on. And

wond-rous love is this that caused the Lord of bliss to
God and to the Lamb who is the great I AM, while
when from death I'm free, I'll sing and joy - ful be, and

A modal song of considerable character which should be sung simply and in unison.

Chords (verse 1): Dm   C   F   Am7(add 2)   Dm   Am
Fmaj7   Em7   Dm7   Am7(add 2)   1.2. Dm   Am7sus   3. Dm

| lay a-side his crown for my soul, for my soul, to |
| mil-lions join the theme, I will sing, I will sing, while |
| through e - ter - ni - ty I'll sing on, I'll sing on, and |

lay a-side his crown for my soul.	2 To
mil-lions join the theme I will sing.	3 And
through e - ter - ni - ty I'll sing	on.

1   What wondrous love is this,
       O my soul, O my soul!
   What wondrous love is this, O my soul!
   What wondrous love is this
      that caused the Lord of bliss
      to lay aside his crown
      for my soul, for my soul,
      to lay aside his crown for my soul.

2   To God and to the Lamb, I will sing, I will sing;
   to God and to the Lamb, I will sing.
   To God and to the Lamb
      who is the great I AM,
      while millions join the theme,
      I will sing, I will sing,
      while millions join the theme I will sing.

3   And when from death I'm free,
       I'll sing on, I'll sing on,
   and when from death I'm free, I'll sing on.
   And when from death I'm free,
      I'll sing and joyful be,
      and through eternity
      I'll sing on, I'll sing on,
      and through eternity I'll sing on.

164

WHEN I BEHOLD JESUS
What kind of love

SOUTH AMERICA

Words: adapted Word & Music
Music: Almaz Belhu
arranged Geoff Weaver

1 When I be-hold Je - sus Christ my Lord who
2 For me you gave all your love, for me you
3 Your hands and feet, all were nailed to that

died for me, I am a - mazed
suf - fered pain; I find no words –
rug - ged cross; you died my death,

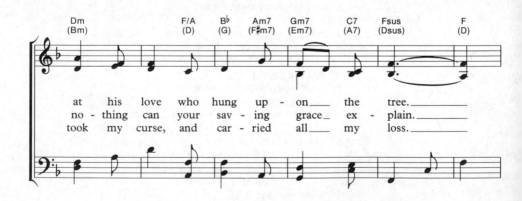

at his love who hung up - on the tree.
no - thing can your sav - ing grace_ ex - plain.
took my curse, and car - ried all my loss.

This pentatonic melody from South America
requires an easy expressive flow.

What kind of love_ is this;_____ what kind of love_ is

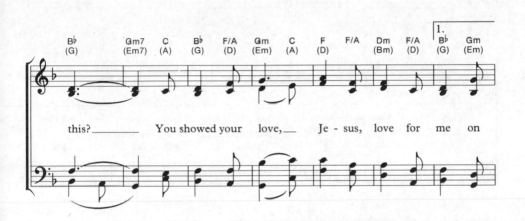

this?_____ You showed your love,_ Je - sus, love for me on

Cal - va - ry._____ What me on Cal - va - ry._____

4 You had no sin, holy Lamb,
   but you were tortured, tried;
   on Golgotha once for all,
   O Son of God, you died.
   SOLO What kind of love . . .
   ALL   What kind of love . . .

5 Incarnate Lord, love come down
   to walk our earthly ways:
   we worship you, speak your name,
   and lift to heaven our praise.
   SOLO What kind of love . . .
   ALL   What kind of love . . .

165 WILL YOU COME AND FOLLOW ME

SCOTLAND

KELVINGROVE

Words: John L. Bell and Graham Maule
Music: Scottish melody
arranged David Peacock

Flowing ♩. = 70

Capo 3(D)

1 Will you come and fol - low me if I but
2 Will you leave your - self be - hind if I but
3 Will you let the blind - ed see if I but

call your name;____ will you go where
call your name;____ will you care for
call your name;____ will you set the

you don't know and ne - ver be the
cruel and kind and ne - ver be the
pris - oners free and ne - ver be the

same?_____ Will you let my love be
same?_____ Will you risk the hos - tile
same?_____ Will you kiss the lep - er

This song may be used effectively at times of commitment.

From the *Heaven shall not wait* collection

Music arrangement: © 1994 David Peacock / Jubilate Hymns   Words: © 1987 WGRG Iona Community, Glasgow G51 3UU

shown,_____ will you let my name be
stare =_____ should your life at - tract or
clean,_____ and do such as this un -

known,___ will you let my life be grown in
scare?___ Will you let me ans - wer prayer in
- seen,___ and ad - mit to what I mean in

you, and you in me?_____
you, and you in me?_____
you, and you in me?_____

4 Will you love the 'you' you hide
 if I but call your name;
will you quell the fear inside
 and never be the same?
Will you use the faith you've found
 to reshape the world around,
through my sight and touch and sound
 in you, and you in me?

5 Lord, your summons echoes true
 when you but call my name:
let me turn and follow you
 and never be the same.
In your company I'll go
 where your love and footsteps show;
thus I'll move and live and grow
 in you, and you in me.

166 WINTER HAS GONE

CHINA

Words: from Song of Solomon 2,
after Wang Wei-fan, Word & Music
Music: Jia-ou Shengben Lina
arranged Geoff Weaver

1 Win-ter has gone, the night is through, flo-wers are bloom-ing, all birds sing. Why should I wait with doubt and fear? A-rise, my Lord, I'll go with you!

2 Re-veal your light that I may see, your still small voice that I may hear; and like a dove, let joy and peace and love des-cend to dwell with me.

3 And so, my Lord, my mas-ter true, a-mong the flowers of pa-ra-dise I'll find you in the sec-ret place, and in your mer-cy go with you.

The verses of this hymn were written before the cultural revolution in China.
The refrain written in 1982 sings of the dark veil of those years which brought
suffering and death to so many in China, but a dramatic growth in the Church.

'Winter has passed' from *Sound the Bamboo*
Music: © 1982 Asian School of Music, Worship and the Arts

Words: after Wang Wei-fan
© 1995 Word & Music / Jubilate Hymns

Chorus

Je - sus, my joy, my hope, my all, my love, my life e - ter - nal - ly: through death's dark night, close by my side, O dear - est Lord, be close to me.

1 Winter has gone, the night is through,
   flowers are blooming, all birds sing.
   Why should I wait with doubt and fear?
   Arise, my Lord, I'll go with you!
      Jesus, my joy, my hope, my all,
      my love, my life eternally:
      through death's dark night, close by my side,
      O dearest Lord, be close to me.

2 Reveal your light that I may see,
   your still small voice that I may hear;
   and like a dove, let joy and peace
   and love descend to dwell with me.
      Jesus, my joy . . .

3 And so, my Lord, my master true,
   among the flowers of paradise
   I'll find you in the secret place,
   and in your mercy go with you.
      Jesus, my joy . . .

167 YESHU SUPRIYA
Jesus, loving Lord

INDIA

Words: unknown
Music: Indian melody
arranged Geoff Weaver

1st time: vocal melody only
2nd time: vocal with accompaniment

Simply ♩ = 84

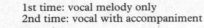

Ye - shu_ su - pri - ya,   Ye - shu_ a - shra - ye.
Je - sus, lov - ing_ Lord;   Je - sus, strength and   stay:

Ye - shu_ pri-ya   ta - ra - ka, sa - ha - ya_ ho - ma - la.
in_ your mer-cy   bless us   all and   keep us_ night and   day.

Yeshu supriya,
Yeshu ashraye.
Yeshu priya taraka,
sahaya homala.

Jesus, loving Lord;
Jesus, strength and stay:
in your mercy bless us all
and keep us night and day.

> A simple song of benediction from India, ideal for the end of an act of worship.

168 YOUR KINGDOM COME, O LORD

RUSSIA

Words and music: N. Zabolotski
arranged John L. Bell

Steadily ♩ = 112

Your king-dom come, O Lord. Your king-dom come, O Lord. Your

king-dom come, O Lord.＿ Your king-dom come, O Lord.

Your kingdom come, O Lord.
Your kingdom come, O Lord.
Your kingdom come, O Lord.
Your kingdom come, O Lord.

Written for a W.C.C. Conference in Melbourne in 1980, the composer Nicolai Zabolotski asked that the song should start softly, almost in a questioning way, and should grow in strength and confidence until the final phrase which asserts the hope that God's Kingdom is coming.

169

YESU YU HAI LEO
Jesus is alive today

EAST AFRICA

Words and music: unknown
arranged David Peacock

Ye-su yu ha-i le-o Ye-su yu ha-i le-o Ye-su
Je-sus is a-live to-day, Je-sus is a-live to-day, Je-sus

yu ha-i le-o a-si-fi-we. Ye-su
is a-live to-day— O praise his name! Je-sus

yu ha-i le-o Ye-su yu ha-i le-o Ye-su
is a-live to-day, Je-sus is a-live to-day, Je-sus

yu ha-i le-o a-si-fi-we.
is a-live to-day— O praise his name!

> An exuberant song from East Africa suitable for Easter Day, or indeed for any day. Harmonies, descants and drum rhythms will naturally suggest themselves.

Al-le - lu-ya,____ al-le - lu-ya, al-le - lu-ya a - si - fi -
Al-le - lu-ia,____ al-le - lu-ia, al-le - lu-ia – O praise his

- we._____ Al - le - lu - ya,____
name!_____ Al - le - lu - ia,____

al-le - lu-ya, al-le - lu-ya a - si - fi - we.
al-le - lu-ia, al-le - lu-ia – O praise his name!

Yesu yu hai leo	Jesus is alive today,
Yesu yu hai leo	Jesus is alive today,
Yesu yu hai leo	Jesus is alive today –
asifiwe.	O praise his name!
Yesu yu hai leo . . .	Jesus is alive . . .
Alleluya, alleluya, alleluya	Alleluia, alleluia, alleluia –
asifiwe.	O praise his name!
Alleluya . . .	Alleluia . . .

170 YUAN QUANNENG ZHU SHANGDI
May the Lord, mighty God

Words: from Numbers 6:24–26, anonymous
Mandarin translation: I-to Loh
Music: Pao-chen Li
arranged Geoff Weaver

CHINA

Gracefully ♩ = 72

1 Yuan quan- neng___ Zhu Shang-di, bao-shou___
1 May the___ Lord,___ might-y God, bless and___

zhu- fu yong bu___ li; ci___ ping-an, wan-
keep you for ev- er; grant you___ peace,___

-quan ping-an, jian-qiang yi- li___ chu wan-nan.
per-fect___ peace, cour-age in ev-ery en-deav- our.

> A song of blessing which is so characteristically Chinese in its melodic shape.
> It is not simple, but repays the effort of learning it.

171 ZAMIRANZA
Alleluia

ZIMBABWE

Words: Shona text
Music: unknown
arranged Geoff Weaver

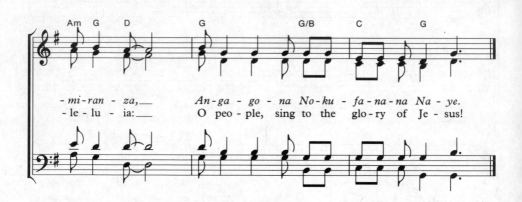

LEADER   *Zamiranza,*
ALL   *Zamiranza, Zamiranza,*
          Angagona
          Nokufanana Naye.

LEADER   Alleluia,
ALL   alleluia, alleluia:
          O people,
          sing to the glory of Jesus!

> The leader-response format is popular throughout Africa. This joyful affirmation requires attack and attention to the syncopated rhythms.

SECTION 2:

INTERNATIONAL

HYMNS AND SONGS

172 ALL HAIL THE POWER
(FIRST TUNE)

CORONATION

Words: after E. Perronet and J. Rippon
in this version Jubilate Hymns
Spanish: verse 1 T. M. Westrup, verses 2–3 L. Berlin
German: Wiard Popkes
Music: Oliver Holden

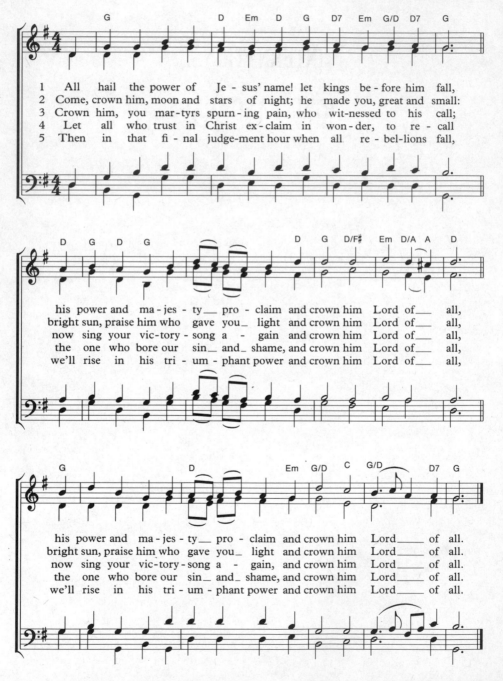

1 All hail the power of Je-sus' name! let kings be-fore him fall,
2 Come, crown him, moon and stars of night; he made you, great and small:
3 Crown him, you mar-tyrs spurn-ing pain, who wit-nessed to his call;
4 Let all who trust in Christ ex-claim in won-der, to re-call
5 Then in that fi-nal judge-ment hour when all re-bel-lions fall,

his power and ma-jes-ty__ pro-claim and crown him Lord of__ all,
bright sun, praise him who gave you__ light and crown him Lord of__ all,
now sing your vic-tory-song a - gain and crown him Lord of__ all,
the one who bore our sin__ and__ shame, and crown him Lord of__ all,
we'll rise in his tri - um - phant power and crown him Lord of__ all,

his power and ma-jes-ty__ pro - claim and crown him Lord____ of all.
bright sun, praise him who gave you__ light and crown him Lord____ of all.
now sing your vic-tory-song a - gain, and crown him Lord____ of all.
the one who bore our sin__ and__ shame, and crown him Lord____ of all.
we'll rise in his tri - um - phant power and crown him Lord____ of all.

ESPAÑOL

1 Loores dad a Cristo el Rey,
suprema potestad;
de su divino amor la ley
postrados aceptad;
de su divino amor la ley
postrados aceptad.

2 Vosotros, hijos de Israel,
ovejas de la grey;
loores dad a Emanuel
y proclamadle Rey;
loores dad a Emanuel
y proclamadle Rey.

3 Gentiles que por su perdón
gozáis de libertad,
al que de la condenación
os libra, hoy load;
al que de la condenación
os libra, hoy load.

4 Naciones todas,
escuchad y obedeced su ley
de gracia y de santidad,
y proclamadle Rey;
de gracia y de santidad,
y proclamadle Rey.

5 Con la celeste multitud
del trono en derredor.
Alzad canción de gratitud
a Cristo el Salvador;
alzad canción de gratitud
a Cristo el Salvador.

DEUTSCH

1 Laut rühmet Jesu Herrlichkeit!
Ihn preist die Engelwelt.
Die Krone bringt und Purpurkleid,
zum Herrn aller Welt,
die Krone bringt und Purpurkleid,
zum Herrn aller Welt.

2 O singet ihm, dem Gotteslamm,
das unsre Nacht erhellt,
und uns erlöst aus Sündenbann,
zum Herrn aller Welt,
und uns erlöst aus Sündenbann,
zum Herrn aller Welt.

3 Auch heute hilft des Heilands Blut
und bringt zum Vater heim,
und machet allen Schaden gut,
zum Herrn aller Welt,
und machet allen Schaden gut,
zum Herrn aller Welt.

4 Ihm diene jedes Volk und Land,
verkündet seinen Ruhm,
und steht für Jesus Hand in Hand,
zum Herrn aller Welt,
und steht für Jesus Hand in Hand,
zum Herrn aller Welt.

5 Einst singen wir in Herrlichkeit,
mit uns die Engelwelt,
und jubelnd klingt's in Ewigkeit:
zum Herrscher aller Welt,
und jubelnd klingt's in Ewigkeit:
zum Herrscher aller Welt.

173 ALL HAIL THE POWER
(SECOND TUNE)

MILES LANE

Words: after E. Perronet and J. Rippon
in this version Jubilate Hymns
Spanish: verse 1 T. M. Westrup, verses 2–3 L. Berlin
German: Wiard Popkes
Music: Later form of melody by W. Shrubsole

1 All hail the power of Je-sus' name! let kings be-fore him fall,
2 Come, crown him, moon and stars of_ night; he made you, great and small:
3 Crown him, you mar-tyrs spurn-ing_ pain, who wit-nessed to his call;
4 Let all who trust in Christ ex-claim in won-der,_ to re-call
5 Then in that fi-nal judge-ment hour when all re-bel-lions fall,

his power and ma-jes-ty__ pro-claim and crown him,
bright sun, praise him who gave_ you_ light and crown him,
now sing your vic-tory - song_ a - gain and crown him,
the one who bore our sin_ and_ shame, and crown him,
we'll rise in his tri - um - phant power and crown him,

crown him, crown__ him, crown him Lord of__ all.
crown him, crown__ him, crown him Lord of__ all.
crown him, crown__ him, crown him Lord of__ all.
crown him, crown__ him, crown him Lord of__ all.
crown him, crown__ him, crown him Lord of__ all.

1 *Loores dad a Cristo el Rey,*
  suprema potestad;
  de su divino amor la ley
  postrados aceptad,
  postrados aceptad.

2 *Vosotros, hijos de Israel,*
  ovejas de la grey;
  loores dad a Emanuel
  y proclamadle Rey,
  y proclamadle Rey.

3 *Gentiles que por su perdón*
  gozáis de libertad,
  al que de la condenación
  os libra, hoy load,
  os libra, hoy load.

4 *Naciones todas,*
  escuchad y obedeced su ley
  de gracia y de santidad,
  y proclamadle Rey,
  y proclamadle Rey.

5 *Con la celeste multitud*
  del trono en derredor.
  Alzad canción de gratitud
  a Cristo el Salvador,
  a Cristo el Salvador.

1 *Laut rühmet Jesu Herrlichkeit!*
  Ihn preist die Engelwelt.
  Die Krone bringt und Purpurkleid.
  O krönt ihn, krönt ihn, krönt ihn,
  zum Herrn aller Welt.

2 *O singet ihm, dem Gotteslamm,*
  das unsre Nacht erhellt,
  und uns erlöst aus Sündenbann.
  O krönt ihn, krönt ihn, krönt ihn,
  zum Herrn aller Welt.

3 *Auch heute hilft des Heilands Blut*
  und bringt zum Vater heim,
  und machet allen Schaden gut.
  O krönt ihn, krönt ihn, krönt ihn,
  zum Herrn aller Welt.

4 *Ihm diene jedes Volk und Land,*
  verkündet seinen Ruhm,
  und steht für Jesus Hand in Hand.
  O krönt ihn, krönt ihn, krönt ihn,
  zum Herrn aller Welt.

5 *Einst singen wir in Herrlichkeit,*
  mit uns die Engelwelt,
  und jubelnd klingt's in Ewigkeit:
  O krönt ihn, krönt ihn, krönt ihn,
  zum Herrn aller Welt.

174 ALL HEAVEN DECLARES

Words and music: Noel and Tricia Richards
Spanish and German: authorized translations

Majestically

1 All heaven de-clares
2 I will pro-claim

the glo-ry of the ri-sen Lord. Who can com-
the glo-ry of the ri-sen Lord, who once was

-pare   with the beau-ty of the Lord?
slain   to re-con-cile___ us to God.

For ev-er he will be   the Lamb up-on the
For ev-er you will be   the Lamb up-on the

throne: I glad-ly bow the knee
throne: I glad-ly bow the knee

and wor-ship him a-lone.
and wor-ship you a-lone.

last time

ESPAÑOL

1 ¿Quién contará
la gloria y el poder de Dios?
¿Quién puede ser
comparado a mi Señor?
La gloria del Señor
siempre perduará.
Me inclinaré ante él,
ante su Majestad.

2 Proclamaré la gloria
y el poder de Dios.
Pues él murió para
darme salvación.
La gloria del Señor
siempre perdurará.
Me inclinaré ante él,
ante su Majestad.

DEUTSCH

1 Der Himmel zeugt
von der Herrlichkeit des Herrn der Herr'n.
Wer ist ihm gleich,
dem einzig Auferstandenen?
In Ewigkeit bist du
das Lamm auf Gottes Thron!
Ich beuge meine Knie
und bete an den Sohn.

2 Verkündigt laut
die Herrlichkeit des Herrn der Herr'n,
der geopfert ward,
die Menschheit zu erlösen.
In Ewigkeit bist du
das Lamm auf Gottes Thron!
Ich beuge meine Knie
und bete an den Sohn.

175 AMAZING GRACE

Words: verses 1–3 John Newton
in this version Jubilate Hymns
verse 4 from *Collection of Sacred Ballads*
Spanish: Casa Bautista de Publicaciones
German: Anton Schulte
Music: *Southern Harmony* 1835
arranged John Barnard

1 A - maz - ing grace — how sweet the sound – that saved a
2 God's grace first taught my heart to fear, his grace my
3 Through ev - ery dan - ger, trial and snare I have al -
4 When we've been there ten thou - sand years, bright shin - ing

wretch like me! I once was lost, but
fears re - lieved: how pre - cious did that
-rea - dy come; for grace has brought me
as the sun, we've no less days to

now am found; was blind, but now I see.
grace ap - pear the hour I first be - lieved!
safe thus far, and grace will lead me home.
sing God's praise than when we first be - gun.

Words: verses 1–3 © in this version Jubilate Hymns
Spanish: © 1978 Casa Bautista de Publicaciones

1   Oh gracia admirable, ¡dulce es!
    ¡Que a mí, pecador, salvó!
    Perdido estaba yo, mas vino a sus pies;
    fui ciego, visión me dio.

2   La gracia me enseñó a temer;
    del miedo libre fui.
    ¡Cuán bella esa gracia fue en me ser,
    la hora en que creí!

3   Peligro, lucha y tentación,
    por fin los logré pasar;
    la gracia me libró de perdición,
    y me llevará al hogar.

4   Después de años mil de estar allí,
    en luz como la del sol:
    podremos cantar por tiempo sin fin
    las glorias del Señor.

1   O Gnade Gottes, wunderbar
    hast du errettet mich.
    Ich war verloren ganz und gar,
    war blind, jetzt sehe ich.

2   Die Gnade hat mich Furcht gelehrt
    und auch von Furcht befreit,
    seitdem ich mich zu Gott bekehrt
    bis hin zur Herrlichkeit.

3   Durch Schwierigkeiten mancher Art
    wurd' ich ja schon geführt,
    doch hat die Gnade mich bewahrt,
    die Ehre Gott gebührt.

4   Wenn wir zehntausend Jahre sind
    in seiner Herrlichkeit,
    mein Herz noch von der Gnade singt
    wie in der ersten Zeit.

BE STILL, FOR THE PRESENCE

Words and music: David J. Evans
Spanish and German: authorized translations
arranged Geoff Baker

Unhurried

1 Be still, for the pres-ence of the Lord, the ho-ly One, is here;
2 Be still, for the glo-ry of the Lord is shin-ing all a-round;
3 Be still, for the pow-er of the Lord is mov-ing in this place:

come bow be-fore him now with re-ver-ence and fear:
he burns with ho-ly fire, with splen-dour he is crowned:
he comes to cleanse and heal, to mi-ni-ster his grace –

in him no sin is found – we stand on ho-ly ground.
how awe-some is the sight – our rad-iant king of light!
no work too hard for him. In faith re-ceive from him.

Be still, for the pres-ence of the Lord, the ho-ly One, is here.
Be still, for the glo-ry of the Lord is shin-ing all a-round.
Be still, for the pow-er of the Lord is mov-ing in this place.

ESPAÑOL

1 Estad quietos
ante el Señor, el Santo de Israel.
Postrémonos ante él
con reverencia.
No hay pecado en él,
irradia santidad.
Estad quietos
ante el Señor, el Santo de Israel.

2 Estad quietos
en su gloria, resplandece su luz.
Arde el fuego santo
él reina con poder.
Maravilloso es
nuestro Rey de luz.
Estad quietos
en su gloria, resplandece su luz.

3 Estad quietos
ante su poder, se está moviendo aquí.
Él viene a sanar,
a damos su favor.
Todo lo puede hacer
si tienes fe en él.
Estad quietos
ante su poder, se está moviendo aquí.

DEUTSCH

1 Seid still,
vor dem Angesicht des Herrn,
der Heilige ist da.
Fallt nieder und betet an:
Gott selber kommt uns nah.
Bringt Ehre, Preis und Ruhm,
ihr seid sein Eigentum.
Seid still,
vor dem Angesicht des Herrn,
der Heilige ist da.

2 Seid still,
denn die Herrlichkeit des Herrn
erfüllt die ganze Welt;
ein heiliges Feuer brennt
und alles wird erhellt.
Wir sehn sein Angesicht
umstrahlt von lauter Licht.
Seid still,
denn die Herrlichkeit des Herrn
erfüllt die ganze Welt.

3 Seid still
denn es weht der Geist des Herrn
und wirkt an diesem Ort:
er reinigt und heilt in Kraft
aus Gnade durch sein Wort.
Kein Werk is ihm zu schwer,
auf Glauben handelt er.
Seid still,
denn es weht der Geist des Herrn
und wirkt an diesem Ort.

177 BLESSED BE THE TIE

DENNIS

Words: John Fawcett
Spanish: unknown
German: Julius Carl Grimmel
Music: Johann G. Nägeli
arranged Lowell Mason

1 Blessed be____ the tie____ that binds our hearts____ in
2 Be - fore____ our Fa - ther's throne we pour____ our
3 We share____ our mu - - tual woes, our mu - tual
4 When for____ a while____ we part, this thought will

Christ - ian love. The fel - low - ship____ of
ar - dent prayers; our fears,____ our hopes,____ our
bur - dens bear, and oft - en for____ each
soothe____ our pain, that we____ shall still____ be

kin - dred hearts____ is like____ to that____ a - bove.
aims____ are one,____ our com - forts and____ our cares.
oth - er flows____ the sym - pa - thi - zing tear.
joined____ in heart____ and hope____ to meet____ a - gain.

1 Sagrado es el amor
   que nos ha unido aquí,
   a los que oímos del Señor
   la fiel palabra, sí.

2 A nuestro Padre Dios,
   rogamos con fervor,
   alúmbrenos la misma luz,
   nos una el mismo amor.

3 Nos vamos a ausentar,
   mas nuestra firme unión,
   jamás podrase quebrantar
   por la separación.

4 Concédenos, Señor,
   la gracia y bendición
   del padre, hijo redentor
   y del consolador.

1 Gesegnet sei das Band,
   das uns im Herrn vereint!
   Geknüpft von Christi Liebeshand,
   bleibts fest, bis er erscheint.

2 Vor unsers Vaters Thron
   steigt ernstlich unser Flehn,
   in Leid und Freud ein Herz, ein Geist,
   so klingts dem Vater schön.

3 Wir tragen jede Last
   mit Schwergeprüften gern;
   des Mitleids Tränen fließen oft
   vereint vor unsern Herrn.

4 Und scheiden wir althier,
   so gibts uns tiefen Schmerz,
   doch bleiben wir im Geist vereint
   und pilgern himmelwärts.

178 CHANGE MY HEART

Words and music: Eddie Espinosa
Spanish and German: authorized translations
arranged James Gabriel Stipech

Prayerfully

Change my heart, O God,_____

_____ make it ev - er true;_____

change my heart, O God,_____

_____ may I be like you.   You are the

pot - ter, I am the clay; mould me and make me, this is what I pray. this is what I pray. you.

CODA slower

ESPAÑOL

ESPAÑOL
    Dame un corazón,
    renovado en ti;
    dame un corazón,
    consagrado a ti.
      Tú el alfarero,
      yo el barro soy;
      ven y moldéame,
      está es mi oración.
    Dame un corazón . . .

DEUTSCH
    Mach mich neu, oh Herr,
    laß mich wahrhaft sein;
    mach mich neu, oh Herr,
    mach mich wie dich rein.
      Du bist der Töpfer,
      Ich bin der Ton;
      form' mich und breche mich,
      so werd' ich schön.
    Mach mich neu, oh Herr . . .

179 CROWN HIM WITH MANY CROWNS

DIADEMATA

Words: M. Bridges and G. Thring
in this version Word & Music
Spanish: E.A. Strange
German: Günter Balders
Music: G. J. Elvey

1 Crown him with many crowns, the Lamb upon the
2 Crown him the Lord of peace – his kingdom is at
3 Crown him the Lord of years, the potentate of

throne, while heaven's eternal anthem drowns all
hand; from pole to pole let warfare cease and
time, creator of the rolling spheres in

music but its own! Awake my soul, and
Christ rule every land! A city stands on
majesty sublime: all hail Redeemer,

sing of him who died to be your saviour and your
high, his glory it displays, and there the nations
hail, for you have died for me; your praise shall never,

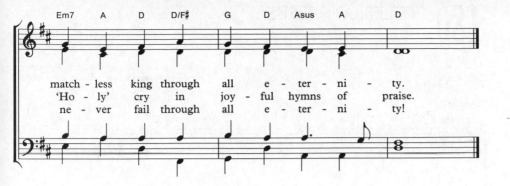

match - less king through all e - ter - ni - ty.
'Ho - ly' cry in joy - ful hymns of praise.
ne - ver fail through all e - ter - ni - ty!

ESPAÑOL

1 *Al Salvador Jesús*
   canciones por doquier,
   con gratitud y puro amor
   entone todo ser;
   a quien nos redemió
   en santa caridad,
   cristianos todos, con ardor,
   su nombre celebrad.

2 *Las glorias declarad*
   del Príncipe de paz;
   es su justicia salvación
   y su poder, bondad.
   Es digno soló él
   de gloria sin igual,
   pues con su sangre nos abrió
   el reino celestial.

3 *A Cristo el Salvador,*
   rey de la eternidad,
   tributa cantos de loor
   el coro celestial;
   con ellos a una voz,
   con júbilo sin par,
   las glorias de su inmenso amor,
   cristianos, entonad.

DEUTSCH

1 *Krönt Jesus, unsern Herrn,*
   das Lamm auf Gottes Thron!
   Hört, wie im Himmel schon erklingt
   das Lied vom Gottessohn!
   Erwache, Herz, und sing
   von dem, der für dich starb,
   Anbetung, Ruhm und Ehre bring
   dem, der das Heil erwarb.

2 *Krönt Jesus, unsern Herrn,*
   der Frieden uns gebracht
   und dessen Szepter allem Streit
   der Welt ein Ende macht.
   Das Reich ist ewig sein,
   das wir im Glauben sehn;
   bekennen wird es jeder Mund,
   wenn wir dort vor ihm stehn.

3 *Krönt Jesus, unsern Herrn,*
   der uns zuerst geliebt,
   ihn, dessen Liebe allen gilt
   und der die Schuld vergibt.
   Er starb für uns am Kreuz,
   erstand in Herrlichkeit.
   Dem Gotteslamm sei Preis
   und Ehr in alle Ewigkeit.

180 CELEBRATE JESUS

Words and music: Gary Oliver
Spanish and German: authorized translations

Celebrate Jesus, ce-le-brate! Ce-le-brate Jesus, ce-le-brate!

1. He is ris - en, he is

ESPAÑOL

¡Celebrad a Cristo, celebrad!
¡Celebrad a Cristo, celebrad!
¡Celebrad a Cristo, celebrad!
¡Celebrad a Cristo, celebrad!

Él vive, él vive
y por siempre él reinará.
Él vive, él vive,
vamos a celebrar,
nuestro Señor resucitó.

DEUTSCH

Feiert Jesus, kommt feiert ihn!
Feiert Jesus, kommt feiert ihn!
Feiert Jesus, kommt feiert ihn!
Feiert Jesus, kommt feiert ihn!

Auferstanden, auferstanden!
Nun lebt er in Ewigkeit.
Auferstanden, auferstanden!
Kommt und feiert die Auferstehung
unseres Herrn.

181 Delight yourself in the Lord
(Spanish and German versions)

ESPAÑOL
Delélitate en Jehová,
y él te dará tus deseos más profundos.
Delélitate en Jehová,
y él te dará lo mejor.
Delélitate en Jehová . . .

1 *Adorad, agradeced, dadle amor;*
adorad, agradeced, dadle amor.
Delélitate en Jehová . . .

2 *Buscad, servid, dadle amor;*
buscad, servid, dadle amor.
Delélitate en Jehová . . .

3 *Confiad, seguid, dadle amor;*
confiad, seguid, dadle amor.
Delélitate en Jehová . . .
Delélitate en Jehová . . .

DEUTSCH
Freu' dich, ja, freu' dich an Gott,
er wird geben was dein Herz sich nur wünscht;
freu' dich, ja, freu' dich an Gott,
er wird geben, was du brauchst.
Freu' dich, ja, freu' dich an Gott . . .

1 *Lob' ihm, dank' ihm, hab' ihm lieb;*
lob' ihm, dank' ihm, hab' ihm lieb.
Freu' dich, ja, freu' dich an Gott . . .

2 *Such' ihm, dien' ihm, hab' ihm lieb;*
such' ihm, dien' ihm, hab' ihm lieb.
Freu' dich, ja, freu' dich an Gott . . .

3 *Trau' ihm, folg' ihm, hab' ihm lieb;*
trau' ihm, folg' ihm, hab' ihm lieb;
Freu' dich, ja, freu' dich an Gott . . .
Freu' dich, ja, freu' dich an Gott . . .

Music follows overleaf

181 DELIGHT YOURSELF IN THE LORD

Words: from Psalm 37, Phil Potter
Spanish and German:
authorized translations
Music: Phil Potter
arranged Christopher Norton

The chorus and verses may be sung by different groups simultaneously; in which case,
the verse's first time bar needs to be omitted

Spanish and German versions on previous page

Verse

1 Praise him, thank him, give him love; praise him, thank him, give him love.
2 Seek him, serve him, give him love; seek him, serve him, give him love.
3 Trust him, fol-low him, give him love; trust him, fol-low him, give him love.

182 FATHER IN HEAVEN

Blessèd be the Lord God almighty

Words and music: Bob Fitts
Spanish and German: authorized translations
arranged Geoff Baker

Majestically

Fa - ther in hea-ven, how_ we love you:____ we lift your name in all the earth._____ May your king-dom_ be es-tab-lished in our prais-es_____ as your peo-ple_ de-clare your might-y works. Bless-èd be the Lord God al-

ESPAÑOL

Padre del Cielo te amamos,
exaltamos tu nombre en la tierra.
Establece tu Reino en la alabanza
y tu pueblo declare tus palabras.
    Bendito sea el Señor, Dios poderoso,
    quien era, es y ha de venir.
    Bendito sea el Señor, Dios poderoso,
    por siempre reina él.

DEUTSCH

Vater im Himmel, ja, wir lieben dich,
erheben dich in alle Welt.
Möge dein Reich gegründet sein im Lobpreis,
als deine Kinder verkünden wir dein Werk.
    Lobet Gott, den Herrn, den Allmächtigen,
    der war und ist und ewig bleibt.
    Lobet Gott, den Herrn, den Allmächtigen,
    der herrscht in Ewigkeit.

183 FATHER, WE ADORE YOU

Words and music: Terry Coelho
Spanish and German: authorized translations

Slowly, sustained

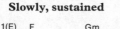

1 Fa - ther, we a - dore you, lay our lives be -
2 Je - sus, we a - dore you, lay our lives be -
3 Spi - rit, we a - dore you, lay our lives be -

- fore you: how we love you!
- fore you: how we love you!
- fore you: how we love you!

This may be sung as a 3-part round.

ESPAÑOL

1 *Padre, te adoramos,*
para tí vivimos,
te amamos.

2 *Cristo, te adoramos . . .*

3 *Espíritu, te adoramos . . .*

DEUTSCH

1 *Vater, wir steh'n vor dir,*
unser Leben gehört dir;
wir lieben dich.

2 *Jesus, wir steh'n vor dir . . .*

3 *Heil'ger Geist, wir steh'n vor dir . . .*

184 FATHER, WE LOVE YOU

Glorify thy name

Words and music: Donna Adkins
Spanish and German: authorized translations
arranged David Peacock

Worshipfully

1 Fa - ther, we love you,
2 Je - sus, we love you, we wor - ship and a - dore you,
3 Spi - rit, we love you,

glo - ri - fy your name in all the earth.

Glo - ri - fy your name, glo - ri - fy your name,

glo - ri - fy your name in all the earth. (all the earth.)

ESPAÑOL

1 *Padre, te amo,*
  te adoro y te alabo.
  Glorifícate en mi Señor.
  Glorifícate,
  glorifícate,
  glorifícate en mi Señor.

2 *Cristo, te amo . . .*

3 *Espíritu, te amo . . .*

DEUTSCH

1 *Vater, ich lieb' dich,*
  ich preise und erhebe dich.
  Herrlich sei dein Name in der Welt!
  Herrlich sei dein Name,
  herrlich sei dein Name,
  herrlich sei dein Name in der Welt.

2 *Jesus, ich lieb' dich . . .*

3 *Heil'ger Geist, ich lieb' dich . . .*

185 FROM HEAVEN YOU CAME
The servant king

Words and music: Graham Kendrick
Spanish and German: authorized translations
arranged David Peacock

Worshipfully

1 From heaven you came, help-less Babe – en-tered our world, your
2 There in the gar-den of tears my hea-vy load he
3 Come see his hands and his feet, the scars that speak of
4 So let us learn how to serve and in our lives en-

glo - ry veiled, not to be served but to serve,
chose to bear; his heart with sor - row was torn,
sac - ri - fice, hands that flung stars in - to space
- throne him, each o - ther's needs to pre - fer –

and give your life that we might live.
'Yet not my will but yours,' he said.
to cru - el nails sur - rend - ered.
for it is Christ we are serv - ing.

This is our

ESPAÑOL

1 *Del cielo tú viniste,*
a nuestro mundo en humildad;
para servir viniste,
y a dar tu vida por nosotros.
   Es nuestro Dios, el Siervo Rey,
   nos llama a seguirle a el,
   brindando nuestras vidas en ofrenda
   de adoración al Siervo Rey.

2 *En el huerto del dolor,*
mi carga escogió llevar;
Su corazón sufrió,
siendo la voluntad de Dios.
   Es nuestro Dios, el Siervo Rey . . .

3 *Mira su cuerpo en la cruz,*
hablando del sacrificio;
clavado fue en la cruz,
rindiéndose por nosotros.
   Es nuestro Dios, el Siervo Rey . . .

4 *Enséñanos a servir,*
y a entronarte en nuestro ser;
nuestro deseo es servir,
a Jesucristo por siempre.
   Es nuestro Dios, el Siervo Rey . . .

DEUTSCH

1 *Vom Himmel kamst du herab*
in eine Welt voll Schuld und Not.
Du kamst als Knecht, nicht als Herr.
Du gabst dein Leben für uns hin.
   Du, unser Gott, Diener und Herr.
   Du rufst uns jetzt, wir folgen dir.
   Täglich soll unser Leben dir gehör'n,
   wir beten an, Diener und Herr.

2 *Dort in Gethsemane*
hat er für mich zu Gott gefleht
Trotz Todesangst, Schmerz und Leid,
ging er gehorsam Gottes Weg.
   Du, unser Gott, Diener und Herr . . .

3 *Schaut seine Wundmale an,*
Hände und Füße sind durchbohrt.
Er, der die Welten erschuf,
starb dort am Kreuz für uns're Schuld.
   Du, unser Gott, Diener und Herr . . .

4 *Herr, gib du uns deinen Sinn:*
Laß uns mit Freuden Diener sein,
und andern helfen in Not,
denn darin ehren wir ja dich.
   Du, unser Gott, Diener und Herr . . .

186 Give thanks
(Spanish and German versions)

ESPAÑOL

Dad gracias de corazón.
Dad gracias al Santo Dios.
Dad gracias porque ha dado
a su Hijo Jesús.
Dad gracias . . .

Y ahora diga el débil, fuerte soy,
diga el pobre, rico soy,
por lo que él hizo en la cruz por mi.
Y ahora . . .
Dad gracias . . .

Y ahora . . .

DEUTSCH

Hab' Dank von Herzen, Herr,
Hab' Dank du Heiliger.
Hab' Dank, denn du gabst Jesus Christus deinen Sohn.
Hab' Dank . . .

In ihm spricht der Schwache: 'Ich bin stark,'
und der Arme: 'Ich bin reich,'
denn was er am Kreuz getan, ist mein!
In ihm . . .
Hab' Dank . . .

In ihm . . .

Music follows overleaf

186 GIVE THANKS

Words and music: Henry Smith
Spanish and German: authorized translations
arranged David Peacock

Spanish and German versions on previous page

187 GOD IS GREAT

Words and music: Graham Kendrick
and Steve Thompson
Spanish and German: authorized translations

His clothing is splendour and majesty bright, for he wraps himself in a garment of light. He spreads out the heavens – his palace of stars, and rides on the wings of the wind.

What marvellous wisdom the Maker displays, the sea vast and spacious, the dolphins and whales, the earth full of creatures, the great and the small, he watches and cares for them all.

The rain forest canopies darken the skies, cathedrals of mist that resound with the choirs of creatures discordant, outrageous, ablaze in colourful pageants of praise.

Above his creation the Father presides: the pulse of the planets, the rhythm of tides, the moon marks the seasons, the day follows night, yet he knows every beat of my heart.

Let cannons of thunder salute their acclaim, the sunsets fly glorious banners of flame, the angels shout 'holy' again and again as they soar in the arch of the heavens.

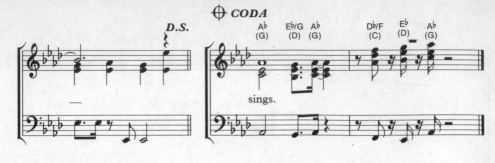

CODA

sings.

ESPAÑOL	DEUTSCH
Grande es Dios, asombroso.	Gott ist groß – und herrlich,
Canten alabanzas.	preist ihn mit Lobgesang,
Grande es Dios, poderoso.	Gott ist groß – erhaben,
Su creación le canta.	die ganze Schöpfung singt!

1. Su ropa es preciosa, con gran majestad
se viste de luz el creador celestial.
Despliega los cielos, castillo estelar,
que muestran su gloria sin par.
    Grande es Dios ...

1. Das Licht ist sein Kleid,
große Pracht sein Gewand,
hell strahlt um ihn her
majestätischer Glanz.
Der Himmel sein Zelt,
sein Sternenpalast –
er zieht auf den Wolken einher!
    Gott ist groß ...

2. Qué sabiduría despliega el creador,
él mar vasto y lleno, ballena y delfín.
La tierra, las plantas, las aves, la flor,
él cuida de todos igual.
    Grande es Dios ...

2. Erstaunliche Weisheit
zeigt Gott überall,
im endlosen Meer,
    beim Delphin und dem Wal.
Geschöpfe verschieden,
ob groß oder klein –
er liebt sie und nennt alle sein!
    Gott ist groß ...

3. Lo espeso del bosque oscurece la luz.
Su bruma resuena en acuerdo coral
de muchas criaturas,
    que en marcha triunfal
desfilan en adoración.
    Grande es Dios ...

3. Der Regenwald steht
wie ein mächtiger Dom,
er birgt soviel Leben
wie kaum anderswo.
Exotische Tiere, laut, schrill und bunt –
gewaltiger Lobpreis erklingt!
    Gott ist groß ...

4. La naturaleza gobierna el Señor,
el ritmo del tiempo, la luna y el sol,
las cuatro estaciones, el frío, el calor,
y el pulso de mi corazón.
    Grande es Dios ...

4. Gott Vater hält alles
fest in seiner Hand,
die Bahn der Planeten,
Gezeitenstand,
die Phasen des Mondes,
den Tag und die Nacht –
selbst mein Herz ist ihm offenbar.
    Gott ist groß ...

5. Cañones de truenos saluden su andar,
carrozas de fuego, guardianes de honor,
los ángeles sean por siempre jamás,
de Dios, el Señor celestial.
    Grande es Dios ...

5. Das Dröhnen des Donners
preist laut seine Macht,
die Sonne geht unter
in glühender Pracht.
Die Engel, sie rufen aus:
Heilig ist er –
allmächtig und würdig der Herr!
    Gott ist groß ...

188 Great is your faithfulness
(Spanish and German versions)

ESPAÑOL

1 Oh, Dios eterno, tu misericordia
ni una sombra de duda tendrá;
tu compasión y bondad nunca fallan
y por los siglos el mismo serás.
    ¡Oh, tu fidelidad! ¡Oh, tu fidelidad!
    Cada momento la veo en mí.
    Nada me falta, pues todo provees,
    ¡Grande, Señor, es tu fidelidad!

2 La noche oscura, el sol y la luna,
las estaciones del año también
unen su canto cual fieles criaturas,
porque eres bueno, por siempre eres fiel.
    ¡Oh, tu fidelidad! . . .

3 Tú me perdonas, me impartes el gozo,
tierno me guías por sendas de paz;
eres mi fuerza, mi fe, mi reposo,
y por los siglos mi Padre serás.
    ¡Oh, tu fidelidad! . . .

DEUTSCH

1 Bleibend ist deine Treu, O Gott mein Vater,
du kennst nicht Schatten,
    noch wechselt dein Licht.
Du bist derselbe, der du warst vor Zeiten,
an deiner Gnade hast niemals gebricht.
    Bleibend ist deine Treu,
        bleibend ist deine Treu.
    Morgen für Morgen
        dein Sorgen ich seh.
    All meinen Mangel hast du mir gestillet,
    bleibend ist deine Treu,
        wo ich auch geh!

2 Ob es der Frühling ist, ob Herbst, ob Winter,
ob ich den Sommer seh in seiner Pracht,
du hast die Welt dir geschaffen zum Zeugnis,
dir nur zum Ruhm und zum Preis deiner Macht.
    Bleibend ist deine Treu . . .

3 Frieden und ewges Heil, Freude die Fülle,
fließt allen Menschen vom Kreuze her zu.
Gott gibt im Fleische sein Liebstes für Sünder,
führet im Opfer die Schöpfung zur Ruh.
    Bleibend ist deine Treu . . .

Music follows overleaf

188 GREAT IS YOUR FAITHFULNESS

Words: T. O. Chisholm
in this version Jubilate Hymns
Spanish: Honorato Reza
German: Wolfgang Zorn
Music: W. M. Runyan

1 Great is your faith-ful-ness, O God my Fa-ther,
2 Sum-mer and win-ter, and spring-time and har-vest,
3 Par-don for sin, and a peace ev-er-last-ing,

you have ful-filled all your pro-mise to me;
sun, moon and stars in their cours-es a-bove,
your liv-ing pres-ence to cheer and to guide;

you ne-ver fail and your love is un-chang-ing—
join with all na-ture in e-lo-quent wit-ness
strength for to-day, and bright hope for to-mor-row—

Spanish and German versions on previous page

189 HE IS EXALTED

Words and music: from Psalm 99, Twila Paris
Spanish and German: authorized translations

Triumphant

He is ex-alt-ed, the King is ex-alt-ed on high – I will

praise_ him. He is ex-alt-ed, for ev-er ex-alt-ed –and

I will praise his name!_____

He is the Lord; for ev-er his truth shall reign;_

hea - ven and earth re - joice in his ho - ly name.

He is ex-alt-ed, the King is ex-alt-ed on high.

190 HE IS LORD

Words and music: Marvin Frey
Spanish: Celebremos / Libros Alianza
German: beim Verfasser
Music arranged Norman Warren
Descant: Angela Reith

Small notes to be used when singing in German.

knee shall bow,___ tongue con - fess___ that

bow, ev - ery tongue con - fess that

Je - sus Christ is Lord.___

Je - sus Christ is Lord.___

ESPAÑOL
Es Señor, es Señor;
Jesucristo resucitó y es Señor.
Rodillas se doblarán,
lenguas confesarán:
que Cristo es el Señor!

DEUTSCH
Er ist Herr, er ist Herr.
Er ist auferstanden, und er ist Herr.
Jedes Knie muß sich beugen,
jede Zunge soll bekennen,
daß Jesus ist der Herr.

191 HOSANNA, HOSANNA

Words and music: Carl Tuttle
Spanish: authorized translation
German: Helga Koenig

1 Ho-san-na, ho-san-na, ho-san-na in the high-est. Ho-
2 Glo-ry, glo-ry, glo-ry to the King of kings;

-san-na, ho-san-na, ho-san-na in the high-est.
Glo-ry, glo-ry, glo-ry to the King of kings:

Lord, we lift up your name, with hearts full of praise.
Lord, we lift up your name, with hearts full of praise.

Be ex-alt-ed, O— Lord my God— ho-san-na in the high-est!
Be ex-alt-ed, O— Lord my God— glo-ry to the King of kings!

ESPAÑOL

1 *Hosanna, hosanna, hosanna en las alturas.*
  Hosanna, hosanna, hosanna en las alturas.
  Yo te alabo Señor,
  con todo mi ser.
  Exaltamos tu nombre, Señor.
  Hosanna en las alturas.

2 *Gloria, gloria, gloria al Rey de reyes.*
  Gloria, gloria, gloria al Rey de reyes.
  Yo te alabo Señor,
  con todo mi ser.
  Exaltamos tu nombre, Señor.
  Hosanna en las alturas.

DEUTSCH

1 *Hosanna, hosanna, hosanna in der Höhe.*
  Hosanna, hosanna, hosanna in der Höhe.
  Du bist König und Herr,
  du regierst mit Macht;
  deine Herrlichkeit ist offenbar,
  hosanna in der Höhe!

2 *Ehre, Ehre, Ehre sei dem König allein.*
  Ehre, Ehre, Ehre sei dem König allein.
  Du bist König und Herr,
  du regierst mit Macht;
  deine Herrlichkeit ist offenbar,
  ehre sei dem König!

192 HOLY, HOLY, HOLY

Nicaea

Words: R. Heber
in this version Word & Music
Spanish: Juan B. Cabrera
German: Günter Balders
Music: J. B. Dykes

1 Ho - ly, ho - ly, ho - ly,___ Lord___ God al - might - y!
2 'Ho - ly, ho - ly, ho - ly!'___ Cry the saints in glo - ry,
3 Ho - ly, ho - ly, ho - ly!___ Sav - iour of the low - ly,
4 Ho - ly, ho - ly, ho - ly,___ Lord___ God al - might - y!

Ear - ly in the morn - ing our song of you shall be:___
cast - ing down their gol - den crowns be - fore the glas - sy sea,___
here the sin - ner's dark - ened eye your glo - ry may not see,___
All your works shall praise your name, in earth and sky and sea:___

ho - ly, ho - ly, ho - ly!___ mer - ci - ful and might - y,
che - ru - bim and se - ra - phim___ sing cre - a - tion's sto - ry:
God of earth and hea - ven,___ you a - lone are ho - ly,
'Ho - ly, ho - ly, ho - ly!___ mer - ci - ful and might - y,

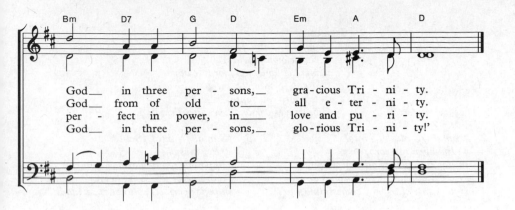

God___ in three per - sons,___ gra - cious Tri - ni - ty.
God___ from of old to___ all e - ter - ni - ty.
per - fect in power, in___ love and pu - ri - ty.
God___ in three per - sons,___ glo - rious Tri - ni - ty!'

TRADITIONAL ENGLISH VERSION

1 Holy, holy, holy, Lord God almighty!
early in the morning
    our song shall rise to thee:
holy, holy, holy! – merciful and mighty,
God in three persons, blessèd Trinity.

2 Holy, holy, holy! All the saints adore thee,
casting down their golden crowns
    around the glassy sea;
cherubim and seraphim
    falling down before thee:
God from of old who evermore shall be!

3 Holy, holy, holy! –
    though the darkness hide thee,
though the eye of sinful man
    thy glory may not see;
only thou art holy, there is none beside thee
perfect in power, in love and purity.

4 Holy, holy, holy, Lord God almighty!
All thy works shall praise thy name,
    in earth and sky and sea:
holy, holy, holy! – merciful and mighty,
God in three persons, blessèd Trinity.

ESPAÑOL

1 ¡Santo! ¡Santo! ¡Santo!
    Señor omnipotente,
siempre el labio mío loores te dará.
¡Santo! ¡Santo! ¡Santo!
    te adoro reverente,
Dios en tres personas, bendita Trinidad.

2 ¡Santo! ¡Santo! ¡Santo!
    En numeroso coro,
santos escogidos te adoran sin cesar,
de alegría llenos, y sus coronas de oro
rinden ante el trono y el cristalino mar.

3 ¡Santo! ¡Santo! ¡Santo!
    Por más que estés velado,
e imposible sea tu gloria contemplar;
santo tú eres solo, y nada hay a tu lado
en poder perfecto, pureza y caridad.

4 ¡Santo! ¡Santo! ¡Santo!
    La gloria de tu nombre
vemos en tus obras en cielo,
    tierra y mar;
¡Santo! ¡Santo! ¡Santo!
    te adorará todo hombre,
Dios en tres personas, bendita Trinidad.

DEUTSCH

1 Heilig, heilig, heilig! Gott, dir sei Ehre!
Dir gilt unser Lob,
    das dich früh am Morgen preist,
heilig, heilig, heilig,
    Herr der Himmelsheere,
gnädig, allmächtig,
    Vater, Sohn und Geist.

2 Heilig, heilig, heilig! singen die Erlösten,
und das Lied des Lammes
    ertönt für allezeit.
Alle Engel dienen dir,
    dem Allerhöchsten,
dem, der da war und ist in Ewigkeit.

3 Heilig, heilig, heilig!
    Unserm Blick entnommen
aus der Welt der Sünder
    dir niemand nahen kann:
du bist voller Liebe
    selbst zu uns gekommen,
dich beten wir als Herrn und Heiland an.

4 Heilig, heilig, heilig!
    Himmel, Land und Meere,
alle Kreatur ihren Schöpfer
    rühmt und preist.
Heilig, heilig, heilig!
    Gott allein die Ehre,
Quell allen Lebens,
    Vater, Sohn und Geist!

193 I am a new creation
(Spanish and German versions)

Español

Mi corazón rebosa,
ya nadie me condena,
    nací de nuevo por Jesús.
Su amor me da la vida,
su paz me reconforta,
    nací de nuevo por Jesús.
Por siempre cantaré,
siempre le alabaré,
proclamaré que mi vida cambió.
Con un eterno gozo
iluminó mi alma
    nací de nuevo por Jesús.

Deutsch

Ich bin eine neue Schöpfung,
ich habe neue Hoffnung,
    durch Gottes Gnade steh' ich hier.
Mein Herz ist voller Liebe,
die ich gern' weitergebe,
    durch Gottes Gnade steh' ich hier.
Ich will dich preisen, Herr,
dich immer preisen, Herr,
für all die Wunder, die du hast getan.
O Herr, ich will dir tanzen,
mit Freud' in meinem Herzen,
    durch Gottes Gnade steh' ich hier!

Music follows overleaf

I AM A NEW CREATION

Words and music: Dave Bilbrough
Spanish and German: authorized translations

With drive

I am a new creation, no more in con-dem-na-tion, here in the grace of God I stand; my heart is o-ver-flow-ing, my love just keeps on grow-ing, here in the grace of God I stand: and I will praise

Spanish and German versions on previous page

194 IN CHRIST THERE IS NO EAST OR WEST

St Peter

Words: from a line by W. A. Dunkerley, Michael Perry
Spanish: from a line by J. Oxenham
German: from a line by J. Oxenham, verses 1–3 Helmut Handt
verse 4 Samuel Rothenburg
Music: A. R. Reinagle

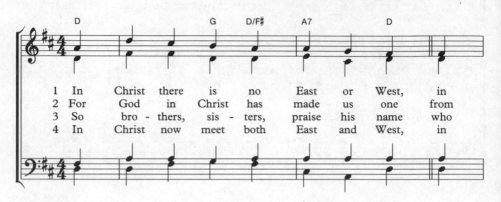

1 In Christ there is no East or West, in
2 For God in Christ has made us one from
3 So bro - thers, sis - ters, praise his name who
4 In Christ now meet both East and West, in

Christ no South or North; but__ on - ly those_ by
ev - ery land and race, has__ re - con - ciled_ us
died to set us free from_ sin, di - vi - sion,
Christ meet South and North – one_ joy - ful peo - ple

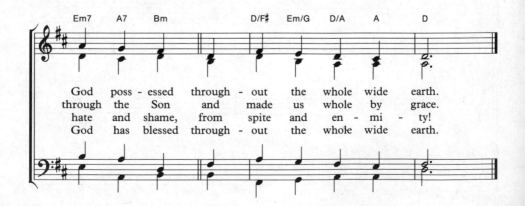

God poss - essed through - out the whole wide earth.
through the Son and made us whole by grace.
hate and shame, from spite and en - mi - ty!
God has blessed through - out the whole wide earth.

ESPAÑOL

1   Oriente ni occidente hay
    en Cristo y su bondad,
    incluida en su amor está
    la entera humanidad.

2   En Dios los fieles al Señor
    su comunión tendrán,
    y con los lazos de su amor
    al mundo ligarán.

3   ¡De razas no haya distinción,
    obreros de la fe!
    El que cual hijo sirve a Dios,
    hermano nuestro es.

4   Oriente y occidente en él
    se encuentran; y su amor
    unió a las almas por la fe
    en santa comunión.

DEUTSCH

1   In Christus ist nicht Ost noch West,
    in ihm nicht Süd noch Nord.
    Er schenkt Gemeinschaft durch sein Maht
    und ruft uns durch sein Wort.

2   Woher wir stammen, fragt er nicht.
    Er lädt zu Brot und Wein,
    bringt alle uns an seinen Tisch,
    und läßt uns eines sein.

3   Drum, Christen, bindet fest den Bund.
    Was trennt, das bleibe fern.
    Wer unserm Vater dienen will,
    der ist verwandt dem Herrn.

4   In Christus trifft sich Ost und West;
    er eint auch Süd und Nord,
    schafft selbst die gute, neue Welt
    und spricht das letzte Wort.

195 IN MY LIFE, LORD
Lord, be glorified

Words and music: Bob Kilpatrick
Spanish and German: authorized translations
arranged David Peacock

ESPAÑOL

1 *En mi vida*
gloria te doy, gloria te doy;
en mi vida
gloria te doy, Señor.

2 *En mi canto*
gloria te doy, gloria te doy;
en mi canto
gloria te doy, Señor.

3 *En tu iglesia*
gloria te doy, gloria te doy;
en tu iglesia
gloria te doy, Señor.

DEUTSCH

1 *Sei verherrlicht*
in meinem Leben, in meinem Leben.
Sei verherrlicht
in meinem Leben Herr!

2 *Sei verherrlicht*
in meinem Nächsten, in meinem Nächsten.
Sei verherrlicht
in meinem Nächsten Herr!

3 *Sei verherrlicht*
in deiner Kirche, in deiner Kirche.
Sei verherrlicht
in deiner Kirche Herr!

196 JESUS, WE ENTHRONE YOU

Lord Jesus, we enthrone you

Words and music: Paul Kyle
Spanish and German: authorized translations
arranged Geoff Baker

With reverence

Je-sus,_____ we en-throne you,_____ we pro-claim you our king _____ stand-ing here_____ in the midst of us! _____ We raise you up_ with our praise._____ And as we

wor - ship, build a throne, and as we wor - ship,

build a throne, and as we wor - ship, build a

throne – come, Lord Je-sus, and take your place!

197 JESUS PUT THIS SONG

Words and music: Graham Kendrick
Spanish and German: authorized translations
arranged Christopher Norton

Hebrew style, getting faster

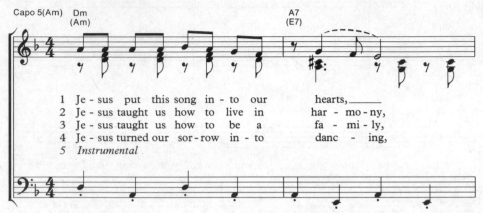

1 Je - sus put this song in - to our hearts,_____
2 Je - sus taught us how to live in har - mo - ny,
3 Je - sus taught us how to be a fa - mi - ly,
4 Je - sus turned our sor - row in - to danc - ing,
5 *Instrumental*

Je - sus put this song in - to our hearts;_____
Je - sus taught us how to live in har - mo - ny;
Je - sus taught us how to be a fa - mi - ly;
Je - sus turned our sor - row in - to dan - cing,

it's a song of joy no - one can take__ a - way__
dif - ferent fa - ces, dif - ferent ra - ces, he made us one__
lov - ing one a - no - ther with the love that he gives__
changed our tears of sad - ness in - to ri - vers of joy__

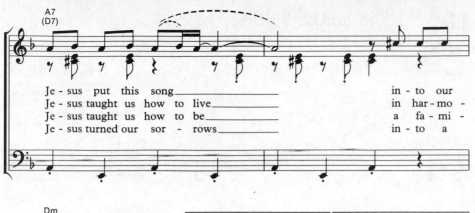

Je - sus put this song _____ in - to our hearts. _____
Je - sus taught us how to live _____ in har - mo - ny. _____
Je - sus taught us how to be _____ a fa - mi - ly. _____
Je - sus turned our sor - rows _____ in - to a dance. _____

ESPAÑOL

1 Cristo puso un canto en nuestro corazón,
Cristo puso un canto en nuestro corazón;
puso en mí un cántico de gozo,
Cristo puso un canto en nuestro ser.

2 Él nos enseñó a vivir en unidad,
él nos enseñó a vivir en unidad;
somos diferentes más él nos unió,
él nos enseñó a vivir en unidad.

3 Él nos enseñó a vivir en familia,
él nos enseñó a vivir en familia;
amándonos con el amor que nos da,
él nos enseñó a vivir en familia.

4 Nuestro dolor en baile, él cambió,
nuestro dolor en baile, él cambió;
nuestro temor cambió en gozo,
nuestro dolor en baile, él cambió.

DEUTSCH

1 Jesus gab ein neues Lied in unser Herz.
Jesus gab ein neues Lied in unser Herz.
Dieses Lied der Freude bleibt in Ewigkeit.
Jesus gab ein Lied – in unser Herz.

2 Jesus lehrt uns, wie man lebt in Harmonie,
Jesus lehrt uns, wie man lebt in Harmonie,
viele Sprachen, viele Länder, er macht uns eins,
Jesus lehrt uns, wie man lebt in Harmonie.

3 Jesus lehrt uns, wie man als Familie lebt,
Jesus lehrt uns, wie man als Familie lebt,
Miteinander Liebe teilen, die er uns gibt,
Jesus lehrt uns, wie man als Familie lebt.

4 Jesus wandelt Traurigkeit in Freudentanz,
Jesus wandelt Traurigkeit in Freudentanz,
Tränen ändert er zu einem Freudenstrom,
Jesus wandelt Traurigkeit in Freudentanz.

198 JESUS SHALL REIGN

DUKE STREET

Words: Isaac Watts
in this version Jubilate Hymns
Spanish: unknown
German: verse 1 H. von Berge,
verses 2–4 Günter Balders
Music: J. Hatton

1 Je - sus shall reign where - 'er the sun
2 Peo - ple and realms of ev - ery tongue
3 To him shall end - less prayer be made,
4 Let all cre - a - tion rise and bring

does his suc - ces - sive jour - neys run; his king - dom stretch from
de - clare his love in sweet - est song, and child - ren's voi - ces
and prin - ces throng to crown his head; his name like in - cense
the high - est hon - ours to our king; ang - els des - cend with

shore to shore till moons shall rise and set no more.
shall pro - claim their ear - ly bless - ings on his name.
shall a - rise with ev - ery morn - ing sac - ri - fice.
songs a - gain and earth re - peat the loud 'A - men!'

1 Doquier alumbre el astro sol
   ha de reinar el Rey Jesús;
   de mar a mar dominará,
   mientras la luna dé su luz.

2 En su bondad meditarán
   pueblos y razas con placer;
   sus bendiciones cantarán
   voces de niños por doquier.

3 Al despertar se elevará
   una plegaria universal,
   y el nombre amado del Señor,
   de paz, la esencia esparcirá.

4 ¡Vengan los hombres a expresar
   su gratitud por tanto bien!
   ¡Vuelvan los cielos a cantar!
   ¡Suene en la tierra un gran Amén!

DEUTSCH

1 Jesus soll Herr und König sein,
   so weit erglänzt der Sonne Schein:
   sein göttlich Reich wird noch bestehn,
   wenn Erd und Himmel untergehn.

2 Menschen aus jedem Volk und Land
   reicht er aus Liebe seine Hand;
   und schon das Lob aus Kindermund
   macht seine Herrschaft allen kund.

3 Ihn krönt Gebet und Lobgesang.
   Ihm gilt auf ewig aller Dank.
   Sein Name fällt des Bösen Fluch
   und füllt die Welt mit Wohlgeruch.

4 Alle Geschöpfe nah und fern,
   bringt euren Dank und preist den Herrn!
   Rühm seinen Namen, Engelheer!
   Welt, singe Amen! Ihm sei Ehr!

199 JOY TO THE WORLD

ANTIOCH

Words: Isaac Watts
Spanish: E. A. Monfort Diaz
German: unknown
Music: G. F. Handel
arranged L. Mason

1 Joy to the world! The Lord has come: let
2 Joy to the earth! The sav - iour reigns: your
3 He rules the world with truth and grace, and

earth re-ceive her king, let ev - ery heart pre-
sweet - est songs em - ploy, while fields and streams and
makes the na - tions prove the glo - ries of his

- pare him room and heaven and na - ture sing, and
hills and plains re - peat the sound-ing joy, re
right - eous - ness, the won - ders of his love, the

and heaven and na - ture
re - peat the sound-ing
the won - ders of his

heaven and na-ture sing, and heaven, and heaven and na-ture sing!
-peat the sound-ing joy, re-peat, re-peat the sound-ing joy.
won-ders of his love, the won-ders, won-ders of his love.

sing, and heaven and na-ture sing, and heaven and na-ture sing!
joy, re-peat the sound-ing joy, re-peat the sound-ing joy.
love, the won-ders of his love, the won-ders of his love.

ESPAÑOL

1 ¡Al mundo paz, nació Jesús!
   Nació ya nuestro rey;
   el corazón ya tiene luz,
     y paz su santa grey,
     y paz su santa grey,
     y paz, y paz su santa grey.

2 ¡Al mundo paz, el Salvador
   en tierra reinará!
   Ya es feliz el pecador,
     Jesús perdón le da,
     Jesús perdón le da,
     Jesús, Jesús perdón le da.

3 Al mundo él gobernará
   con gracia y con poder;
   a las naciones mostrará
     su amor y su poder,
     su amor y su poder,
     su amor, su amor y su poder.

DEUTSCH

1 Freue dich, Welt, dein König naht.
   Mach deine Tore weit!
   An Gnaden reich und hehr an Tat,
     der Herr der Herrlichkeit,
     der Herr der Herrlichkeit,
     der Herr, der Herr der Herrlichkeit!

2 Freue dich, Welt, es siegt der Herr!
   Nun rausche froh dein Sang!
   Von Feld und Flur, von Berg und Meer,
     erschall der Jubelklang,
     erschall der Jubelklang,
     erschall, erschall der Jubelklang!

3 Tag, brich herein! Der Herr gebeut!
   Vorbei der Menschheit Nacht!
   Sein Zepter ist Gerechtigkeit,
     und Lieb' ist seine Macht,
     und Lieb' ist seine Macht,
     und Lieb', und Lieb' ist seine Macht!

200 JUST AS I AM

WOODWORTH

Words: C. Elliott
in this version Jubilate Hymns
Spanish: T. M. Westrup
German: P. W. Birkel
Music: W. B. Bradbury

1 Just as I am, with - out one plea but that you
2 Just as I am, though tossed a - bout with ma - ny a
3 Just as I am, poor, wretch - ed, blind! Sight, rich - es,
4 Just as I am! You will re - ceive, will wel - come,
5 Just as I am! Your love un - known has bro - ken

died to set me free, and at your bid - ding 'Come to
con - flict, many a doubt, fight - ings with - in and fears with -
heal - ing of the mind all that I need, in you to
par - don, cleanse, re - lieve: be - cause your pro - mise I be -
ev - ery bar - rier down: now to be yours, yes, yours a -

me!' O Lamb of God, I come, I come.
- out,
find:
- lieve,
- lone,

1 Tal como soy, de pecador,
   sin más confianza que tu amor,
   y a que me llamas, acudí;
      Cordero de Dios, heme aquí.

2 Tal como soy, buscando paz en mi
   desgracia y mal tenaz,
   conflicto grande siento en mí;
      Cordero de Dios, heme aquí.

3 Tal como soy, con mi maldad,
   miseria, pena y ceguedad;
   pues hay remedio pleno en ti,
      Cordero de Dios, heme aquí.

4 Tal como soy, me acogerás;
   perdón, alivio me darás,
   pues tu promesa ya creí;
      Cordero de Dios, heme aquí.

5 Tal como soy, tu compasión
   vencido ha toda oposición;
   y a pertenezco sólo a ti;
      Cordero de Dios, heme aquí.

1 So wie ich bin, so muß es sein,
   nicht meine Kraft, nur du allein,
   dein Blut wäscht mich von Flecken rein.
      O Gottes Lamm, ich komm, ich komm.

2 So wie ich bin, von Sturm gejagt,
   mit bangen Zweifeln oft geplagt,
   vom Feind bedroht und sehr verzagt.
      O Gottes Lamm, ich komm, ich komm.

3 So wie ich bin, blind, arm und irr',
   such' ich, was mir gebricht, bei dir:
   Licht, Reichtum, deiner Gnade Zier.
      O Gottes Lamm, ich komm, ich komm.

4 Grad' wie ich bin, nimmst du mich an,
   die Sündenschuld ist abgetan,
   weil ich auf dein Wort trauen kann.
      O Gottes Lamm, ich komm, ich komm.

5 Grad' wie ich bin, was mich noch hält,
   vor deiner Lieb in Staub zerfällt,
   dir hab ich ewig mich vermählt.
      O Gottes Lamm, ich komm, ich komm.

201 LORD, THE LIGHT OF YOUR LOVE

Words and music: Graham Kendrick
Spanish and German: authorized translations

Majestic and steady

1 Lord, the light of your love is shin - ing, in the midst of the dark - ness, shin - ing: Je - sus, light of the world, shine up - on___ us; set us free by the truth you now bring___ us –

2 Lord, I come to your awe - some pres - ence, from the sha - dows in - to your ra - diance; by your blood I may en - ter your bright-ness: search me, try me, con - sume all my dark - ness –

3 As we gaze on your king - ly bright-ness so our fa - ces dis - play your like - ness, ev - er chang-ing from glo - ry to glo - ry: mir - rored here, may our lives tell your sto - ry –

Chorus

ESPAÑOL

1 Dios, la luz de tu amor brillando está,
   en el medio de las tinieblas.
   Cristo, tu eres la luz de este mundo;
   líbranos de las negras tinieblas.
   Brilla en mí, brilla en mí.
      Brilla Jesús, reflejando la luz del Padre.
      Espíritu, manda fuego hoy.
      En todo lugar,
      fluyan ríos de misericordia.
      Manda tu poder y que venga la luz.

2 A tu santa presencia vengo,
   de la sombra a tu luz radiante.
   Vengo a ti a través de tu sangre;
   escudriña y prueba mi alma.
   Brilla en mí, brilla en mí.
      Brilla Jesús . . .

3 Contemplando tu faz radiante,
   reflejamos tu luz a otros.
   Transformados de gloria en gloria;
   que otros vean, así, tu imagen.
   Brilla en mí, brilla en mí.
      Brilla Jesús . . .

DEUTSCH

1 Herr, das Licht deiner Liebe leuchtet auf,
   strahlt in mitten der Finsternis für uns auf.
   Jesus, du Licht der Welt, sende uns dein Licht,
   mach uns frei durch die Wahrheit, du jetzt ausbricht
   Sei mein Licht, sei mein Licht!
      Jesus, mein Licht,
      füll dies Land mit des Vaters Ehre!
      Komm, Heil'ger Geist
      setz die Herzen in Brand!
      Fließ Gnadenstrom,
      überflute dies Land mit Liebe,
      sende dein Wort,
      Herr, dein Licht strahle auf!

2 Herr, voll Ehrfurcht komm' ich zu deinem Thron,
   aus dem Dunkel ins Licht des Gottessohns.
   Durch dein Blut kann ich nun vor dir stehen.
   Prüf mich, Herr, laß mein Dunkel vergehen.
   Sei mein Licht, sei mein Licht.
      Jesus, mein Licht . . .

3 Schaun wir, König, zu deinem Glanze auf
   dann strahlt dein Bild auf unser'm Antlitz auf.
   Du hast Gnade um Gnade gegeben,
   dich widerspiegelnd erzählt unser Leben
   von deinem Licht, von deinem Licht!
      Jesus, mein Licht . . .

202 My Lord, what love is this
(Spanish and German versions)

ESPAÑOL

1 Señor, oh que amor
diste por mí;
que yo, un pecador,
libre soy.
  Inmenso amor, que sacrificio,
  El Hijo de Dios, dado por mí.
  Mi deuda pagó, mi muerte él murió,
  y ahora puedo vivir, y ahora puedo vivir.

2 Y ellos le vieron
muerto, burlado;
pero su sangre
me cubrió.
  Inmenso amor . . .

3 Ahora, este amor
fluirá como ríos;
limpia tu iniquidad,
vive en él.
  Inmenso amor . . .

DEUTSCH

1 Mein Gott, du liebst mich so,
daß du dich opferst
für mich, den Schuldigen;
jetzt bin ich frei!
  Welch Liebesstrom und Barmherzigkeit,
  der Gottessohn starb für mich,
  hat die Schuld getilgt, mich vom Tod befreit,
  gab Leben mir ewiglich, gab Leben mir ewiglich!

2 Als er am Kreuz verschied,
verlassen und verachtet,
floß Blut von seinem Leib
als Sühne für mich.
  Welch Liebesstrom und Barmherzigkeit . . .

3 Die Liebe Christi strömt
und schenkt Vergebung,
so komm, bring deine Schuld,
dein Leben wird neu!
  Welch Liebesstrom und Barmherzigkeit . . .

Music follows overleaf

202 MY LORD, WHAT LOVE IS THIS

Words and music: Graham Kendrick
Spanish and German: authorized translations

With strength

1 My Lord, _____ what love is this, _____ that pays _____ so dear - ly, _____ that I, _____ the guil - ty one, _____ may go free! _____

(2) so _____ they watched him die, _____ des - pised, _____ re - ject - ed: _____ but oh, _____ the blood he shed _____ flowed for me! _____

(3) now _____ this love of Christ _____ shall flow _____ like ri - vers: _____ come, wash _____ your guilt a - way, _____ live a - gain! _____

Chorus

A - maz-ing love, _____ oh what

Spanish and German versions on previous page

203 MAJESTY

Words and music: Jack Hayford
Spanish and German: authorized translations

Majestically

Ma - jes - ty —— wor-ship his ma - jes - ty; —— un - to
Je - sus be glo - ry, hon-our and praise! ——
Ma - jes - ty, —— king-dom, au - tho - ri - ty, flow from his
throne un - to his own: his an-them raise! —— So ex -

ESPAÑOL

Majestad, adorad su majestad
a Jesús la gloria, honra y loor.
Majestad, reino y autoridad
fluyen del trono hacia su pueblo.
    A él cantad.
Exaltad y proclamad el nombre de Cristo.
Magnificad, glorificad a Cristo el Rey.
Majestad, adorad su majestad.
Cristo murió, se glorificó
    y es nuestro Rey.

DEUTSCH

Majestät, herrliche Majestät,
dir sei Ehre, Herrlichkeit und Lob.
Majestät, herrliche Majestät,
von dir fließt Kraft in großer Macht
    zu deinem Volk.
Hebt ihn hoch, hebt ihn hoch,
    den Namen Jesus.
Macht ihn groß, kommt
    und verehrt Christus, den Herrn.
Majestät, herrliche Majestät,
Jesus, du bist Herr aller Herr'n,
    Halleluja.

204 O FOR A THOUSAND TONGUES TO SING

FIRST TUNE

LYNGHAM

Words: C. Wesley
Spanish: Esteban Sywulka B.
German: E. Gensichen
Music: T. Jarman

1 O for a thou - sand tongues to sing my great re - deem - er's praise, my great re - deem - er's praise, the glo - ries of my God and

2 Je - sus, the name that charms our fears and bids our sor - rows cease: my bids our sor - rows cease; this mu - sic in the sin - ner's

3 He breaks the pow - er of can - celled sin, he sets the pri - soner free; he sets the pri - soner free; his blood can make the foul - est

king, the tri-umphs of his
ears is life and health and
clean, his blood a-vailed for

the tri-umphs of his grace, the
is life and health and peace, is
his blood a-vailed for me, his

grace, the tri-umphs of___ his___ grace,_____ the
peace, is life and health and___ peace,_____ is
me, his blood a-vailed for___ me,_____ his

tri-umphs of his grace,_____ the tri-umphs of his
life and health and peace,_____ is life and health and
blood a-vailed for me,_____ his blood a-vailed for

tri - umphs of his grace!
life_____ and health and peace.
blood_____ a - vailed for me.

grace, the tri-umphs of his grace!
peace, is life and health and peace.
me, his blood a-vailed for me.

4 Hear him, you deaf! his praise, you dumb,
   your loosened tongues employ;
   you blind, now see your saviour come,
   and leap, you lame, for joy!

5 My gracious Master and my God,
   assist me to proclaim
   and spread through all the earth abroad
   the honours of your name.

1   *¡Oh, que tuviera lenguas mil*
    para poder cantar
    las glorias de mi Dios y rey,
    y sus triunfos alabar!

2   *Su nombre trae consuelo y paz,*
    nos libra del temor;
    salud, aliento y gozo es;
    vida da al pecador.

4   *Oh, mudos, de su amor hablad;*
    y sordos, oíd su voz;
    oh, cojos, de emoción saltad;
    ciegos, ved al Salvador.

3   *Quebranta el poder del mal,*
    al preso libra hoy;
    su sangre limpia al ser más vil,
    ¡Aleluya! limpio estoy.

5   *Señor Jesús, ayúdame*
    tu nombre a proclamar.
    A todo el mundo en derredor,
    tu grandeza ensalzar.

1   *O, hätt' ich tausend Zungen nur,*
    zu rühmen Jesu Tat,
    und seine göttliche Natur,
    die Siege seiner Gnad.

2   *Jesus, dein Nam' verscheucht die Pein,*
    macht aus dem Leid ein Lied,
    dringt wie Musik ins Herz hinein,
    ist Leben, Heil und Fried'.

4   *Ihr Tauben, hört auf Gottes Gnad,*
    ihr Stummen, sprecht, ja, singt,
    ihr Blinden, seht, der Retter naht,
    ihr Lahmen, freudig singt.

3   *Er bricht die Macht der Sündenqual,*
    läßt Hartgebund'ne frei.
    Sein Blut versöhnt die Sünder all,
    dies Blut mein Lobpreis sei.

5   *Mein gnädger Fürst und Gottesheld,*
    in mir die Kraft vermehr',
    zu künden durch die weite Welt,
    Herr, deine Macht und Ehr'.

SECOND TUNE

Words: C. Wesley
Spanish: Esteban Sywulka B.
German: E. Gensichen
Music: Carl Gläser
arranged L. Mason

Azmon

1 O for a thou - sand tongues to sing my
2 Je - sus, the name that charms our fears and
3 He breaks the power of can - celled sin, he
4 Hear him, you deaf! his praise, you dumb, your
5 My gra - cious Mas - ter and my God, as -

great re - deem - er's praise, the glo - ries of my
bids our sor - rows cease: this mu - sic in the
sets the pri - soner free; his blood can make the
loos - ened tongues em - ploy; you blind, now see your
- sist me to pro - claim and spread through all the

God and king, the___ tri - umphs of his grace!
sin - ner's ears is___ life and health and peace.
foul - est clean, his___ blood a - vailed for me.
sav - iour come, and___ leap, you lame, for joy!
earth a - broad the___ hon - ours of your name.

205 O WORSHIP THE KING

FIRST TUNE

HANOVER

Words: from Psalm 104
after W. Kethe, R. Grant
Spanish: S. L. Hernández
German: Günter Balders
Music: W. Croft

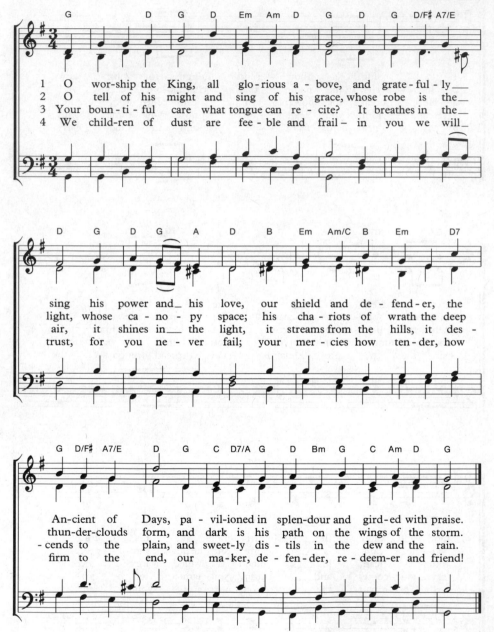

1 O wor-ship the King, all glo-rious a-bove, and grate-ful-ly
2 O tell of his might and sing of his grace, whose robe is the
3 Your boun-ti-ful care what tongue can re-cite? It breathes in the
4 We child-ren of dust are fee-ble and frail – in you we will

sing his power and his love, our shield and de-fend-er, the
light, whose ca-no-py space; his cha-riots of wrath the deep
air, it shines in the light, it streams from the hills, it des-
trust, for you ne-ver fail; your mer-cies how ten-der, how

An-cient of Days, pa-vil-ioned in splen-dour and gird-ed with praise.
thun-der-clouds form, and dark is his path on the wings of the storm.
-cends to the plain, and sweet-ly dis-tils in the dew and the rain.
firm to the end, our ma-ker, de-fen-der, re-deem-er and friend!

1 Al Rey adorad, grandioso Señor,
   y con gratitud cantad de su amor.
   Anciano de días, el gran defensor,
   de gloria vestido, le damos loor.

2 Decid de su amor, su gracia cantad;
   vestido de luz y de majestad.
   Su carro de fuego en las nubes mirad;
   son negras sus huellas en la tempestad.

3 ¿Quién puede tu providencia contar?
   pues tu aire me das para respirar.
   En valles y en montes alumbra tu luz,
   y con gran dulzura me cuida Jesús.

4 Muy frágiles son los hombres aquí,
   mas por tu bondad confiamos en ti.
   Tu misericordia ¡cuán firme! ¡cuán fiel!
   creador, salvador y amigo es él.

1 Erkennt und erhebt den Herrn dieser Welt,
   der alles, was lebt, erschafft und erhält,
   der täglich aufs neue sein Heil offenbart.
   Rühmt laut seine Treue: er hat uns bewahrt.

2 Erzählt, was er tut besingt seine Macht:
   Die Werke sind gut, die er sich erdacht;
   er ordnet sie weise, sie sind ungezählt.
   Ihn lobe und preise mit uns seine Welt.

3 Geschöpfe weltweit erwarten von Gott
   zur richtigen Zeit das tägliche Brot;
   wo er sich abwendet, da sind sie verstört,
   doch alle Not endet, wenn er sie erhört.

4 Verblaßt mancher Stern und Berge vergehn:
   Die Ehre des Herrn bleibt immer bestehn,
   sein Lob wird erklingen in Ewigkeit hin.
   Dem Herrn will ich singen, solange ich bin.

SECOND TUNE

LYONS

Words: from Psalm 104
after W. Kethe, R. Grant
Spanish: S. L. Hernández
German: Günter Balders
Music: W. Gardiner's Sacred Melodies
arranged J. Haydn

1 O wor-ship the King, all glo-rious a-bove, and grate-ful-ly
2 O tell of his might and sing of his grace, whose robe is the
3 Your boun-ti-ful care what tongue can re-cite? It breathes in the
4 We child-ren of dust are fee-ble and frail— in you we will

sing his power and his love, our shield and de-fend-er, the
light, whose ca-no-py space; his cha-riots of wrath the deep
air, it shines in the light, it streams from the hills, it des-
trust, for you ne-ver fail; your mer-cies how ten-der, how

An-cient of Days, pa-vil-ioned in splen-dour and gird-ed with praise.
thun-der-clouds form, and dark is his path on the wings of the storm.
-cends to the plain, and sweet-ly dis-tils in the dew and the rain.
firm to the end, our ma-ker, de-fend-er, re-deem-er and friend!

ESPAÑOL

1 *Al Rey adorad, grandioso Señor,*
  y con gratitud cantad de su amor.
  Anciano de días, el gran defensor,
  de gloria vestido, le damos loor.

2 *Decid de su amor, su gracia cantad;*
  vestido de luz y de majestad.
  Su carro de fuego en las nubes mirad;
  son negras sus huellas en la tempestad.

3 *¿Quién puede tu providencia contar?*
  pues tu aire me das para respirar.
  En valles y en montes alumbra tu luz,
  y con gran dulzura me cuida Jesús.

4 *Muy frágiles son los hombres aquí,*
  mas por tu bondad confiamos en ti.
  Tu misericordia ¡cuán firme! ¡cuán fiel!
  creador, salvador y amigo es él.

DEUTSCH

1 *Erkennt und erhebt den Herrn dieser Welt,*
  der alles, was lebt, erschafft und erhält,
  der täglich aufs neue sein Heil offenbart.
  Rühmt laut seine Treue: er hat uns bewahrt.

2 *Erzählt, was er tut besingt seine Macht:*
  Die Werke sind gut, die er sich erdacht;
  er ordnet sie weise, sie sind ungezählt.
  Ihn lobe und preise mit uns seine Welt.

3 *Geschöpfe weltweit erwarten von Gott*
  zur richtigen Zeit das tägliche Brot;
  wo er sich abwendet, da sind sie verstört,
  doch alle Not endet, wenn er sie erhört.

4 *Verblaßt mancher Stern und Berge vergehn:*
  Die Ehre des Herrn bleibt immer bestehn,
  sein Lob wird erklingen in Ewigkeit hin.
  Dem Herrn will ich singen, solange ich bin.

206 O LORD MY GOD
How great thou art

Words: from a Russian hymn
Stuart K. Hine
Spanish and German:
authorized translations
music arranged Stuart K. Hine

1 O Lord my God, when I in awe - some
2 When through the woods and for - est glades I
3 And when I think that God his Son not
4 When Christ shall come with shout of ac - cla -

won - der con - sid - er all the works thy hand hath
wan - der and hear the birds sing sweet - ly in the
spar - ing, sent him to die — I scarce can take it
- ma - tion and take me home — what joy shall fill my

made;_____ I see the stars, I hear the might - y
trees;_____ when I look down from loft - y moun - tain
in._____ That on the cross my bur - den glad - ly
heart!_____ Then I shall bow in hum - ble a - do -

1   Señor, mi Dios, al contemplar los cielos,
    el firmamento y las estrellas mil,
    Al oír tu voz en los potentes truenos
    y ver brillar el sol en su cenit.
        Mi corazón entona la canción,
        ¡Cuán grande es él!
            ¡Cuán grande es él!
        Mi corazón entona la canción,
        ¡Cuán grande es él!
            ¡Cuán grande es él!

2   Al recorrer los montes y los valles
    y ver las bellas flores al pasar,
    Al escuchar el canto de las aves
    y el murmurar del claro manantial.
        Mi corazón entona la canción . . .

3   Cuando recuerdo del amor divino
    que desde el cielo al Salvador envió,
    Aquel Jesús que por salvarme vino
    y en una cruz sufrió por mí y murió.
        Mi corazón entona la canción . . .

4   Cuando el Señor me llame a su presencia,
    al dulce hogar, al cielo de esplendor,
    le adoraré cantando la grandeza
    de su poder y su infinito amor.
        Mi corazón entona la canción . . .

1   Du großer Gott, wenn ich die Welt betrachte,
    die du geschaffen durch dein Allmachtswort,
    wenn ich auf alle jene Wesen achte,
    die du regierst und nährest fort und fort.
        Dann jauchzt mein Herz dir,
            großer Herrscher zu:
        wie groß bist du, wie groß bist du.
        Dann jauchzt mein Herz dir
            großer Herrscher zu:
        wie groß bist du, wie groß bist du.

2   Blick' ich empor zu jenen lichten Welten
    und seh' der Sterne unzählbare Schar,
    wie Sonn' und Mond im lichten Äther zelten,
    gleich gold'nen Schiffen hehr und wunderbar.
        Dann jauchzt mein Herz dir . . .

3   Wenn mir der Herr in seinem Wort begegnet,
    wenn ich die großen Gnadentaten seh',
    wie er das Volk des Eigentums gesegnet,
    wie er's geliebt begnadigt je und je.
        Dann jauchzt mein Herz dir . . .

4   Und seh' ich Jesus auf der Erde wandeln,
    in Knechtsgestalt, voll Lieb' und großer Huld,
    wenn ich im Geiste seh' sein göttlich Handeln,
    am Kreuz bezahlen vieler Sünder Schuld.
        Dann jauchzt mein Herz dir . . .

207 Oh, heaven is in my heart
(Spanish and German versions)

ESPAÑOL

¡Oh, el cielo está en mi ser,
Oh, el cielo está en mi ser!
¡Oh, el cielo está en mi ser ...

LEADER *El Reino de Dios está aquí,*
ALL *el cielo está en mi ser;*
LEADER *la presencia de su gloria,*
ALL *el cielo está en mi ser;*
LEADER *y en su presencia gozo hay,*
ALL *el cielo está en mi ser;*
LEADER *la luz de la santidad,*
ALL *¡el cielo está en mi ser!*
¡Oh, el cielo está en mi ser ...

LEADER	*Su preciosa vida me dio,*		WOMEN	*Somos templo de su trono,*
ALL	*el cielo está en mi ser;*		ALL	*el cielo está en mi ser;*
LEADER	*para darme vida sin fin,*		WOMEN	*y Cristo es el cimiento,*
ALL	*el cielo está en mi ser;*		ALL	*el cielo está en mi ser;*
LEADER	*mi confianza en Cristo está,*		WOMEN	*y a por nosotros Él vendrá*
ALL	*el cielo está en mi ser;*		ALL	*el cielo está en mi ser;*
LEADER	*y toda nuestra heredad,*		WOMEN	*el Espíritu dice: ¡Ven!*
ALL	*¡el cielo está en mi ser!*		ALL	*¡el cielo está en mi ser!*
	¡Oh, el cielo está en mi ser ...			*¡Oh, el cielo está en mi ser ...*

DEUTSCH

Oh, der Himmel erfüllt mein Herz!
Oh, der Himmel erfüllt mein Herz!
Oh, der Himmel erfüllt mein Herz ...

LEADER *Das Reich des Herrn is unter uns:*
ALL *der Himmel erfüllt mein Herz;*
LEADER *der Glanz von seiner Majestät,*
ALL *der Himmel erfüllt mein Herz;*
LEADER *die Freude seiner Gegenwart,*
ALL *der Himmel erfüllt mein Herz;*
LEADER *die Heiligkeit die von ihm strahlt,*
ALL *der Himmel erfüllt mein Herz!*
Oh, der Himmel erfüllt mein Herz ...

LEADER *Sein Leben gab er für mich hin,*
ALL *der Himmel erfüllt mein Herz;*
LEADER *damit ich ewig leben kann.*
ALL *Der Himmel erfüllt mein Herz;*
LEADER *Ja, Jesus gibt mir Zuversicht,*
ALL *der Himmel erfüllt mein Herz.*
LEADER *Sein Wort steht fest und gilt für mich*
ALL *der Himmel erfüllt mein Herz!*
Oh, der Himmel erfüllt mein Herz ...

WOMEN *Wir sind der Tempel seines Throns',*
ALL *der Himmel erfüllt mein Herz;*
WOMEN *und Jesus ist das Fundament,*
ALL *der Himmel erfüllt mein Herz;*
WOMEN *Er kehrt zurück und holt uns heim,*
ALL *der Himmel erfüllt mein Herz;*
WOMEN *der Geist, die Braut, sie sprechen: Komm!*
ALL *der Himmel erfüllt mein Herz!*
Oh, der Himmel erfüllt mein Herz ...

Music follows overleaf

207 OH, HEAVEN IS IN MY HEART

Words and music: Graham Kendrick
Spanish and German: authorized translations

Oh,_____ hea-ven is in__ my heart!

Oh,_____

hea-ven is in__ my heart!_

LEADER 1   The
LEADER 2   His
WOMEN 3   We

king-dom of__ our God__ is here,
pre-cious life__ on me__ / he spent,
are a tem - ple for__ his throne,

ALL hea-ven is in__ my heart;

Spanish and German versions on previous page

208 PRAISE, MY SOUL

REGENT SQUARE

Words: from Psalm 103, H. F. Lyte
Spanish: R. E. Ríos
German: Günter Balders
Music: H. T. Smart

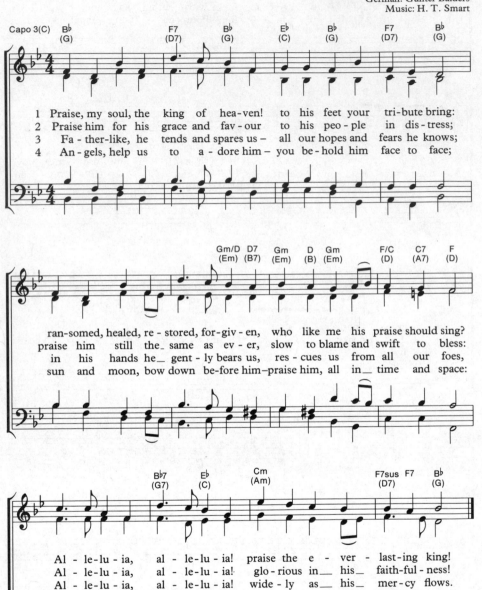

1 Praise, my soul, the king of hea-ven! to his feet your tri-bute bring:
2 Praise him for his grace and fav-our to his peo-ple in dis-tress;
3 Fa-ther-like, he tends and spares us – all our hopes and fears he knows;
4 An-gels, help us to a-dore him – you be-hold him face to face;

ran-somed, healed, re-stored, for-giv-en, who like me his praise should sing?
praise him still the same as ev-er, slow to blame and swift to bless:
in his hands he gent-ly bears us, res-cues us from all our foes,
sun and moon, bow down be-fore him–praise him, all in time and space:

Al-le-lu-ia, al-le-lu-ia! praise the e-ver-last-ing king!
Al-le-lu-ia, al-le-lu-ia! glo-rious in his faith-ful-ness!
Al-le-lu-ia, al-le-lu-ia! wide-ly as his mer-cy flows.
Al-le-lu-ia, al-le-lu-ia! praise with us the God of grace!

1 Canta, canta, alma mía,
a tu Rey y tu Señor;
reconoce sus bondades;
te bendice con favor.
   Canta, canta, alma mía,
canta de su gran amor.

2 Canta su misericordia,
que a tus padres protegió;
en su amor te dio la vida,
te cuidó y perdonó.
   Canta, canta, alma mía,
canta al Dios que te salvó.

3 Como padre te conoce,
sabe tu debilidad,
con su brazo te conduce,
te protege de maldad.
   Canta, canta, alma mía,
canta su fidelidad.

4 Angeles y querubines,
que su majestad cantáis,
oh, estrellas, sol y luna,
que los cielos domináis.
   Todos juntos, alabemos,
adorando a nuestro Dios.

DEUTSCH

1 Preis sei Gott mit Lied und Leben:
Er hat Gutes uns getan,
er hat unsere Schuld vergeben,
uns geheilt nach seinem Plan.
   Preis und Ehre, Preis und Ehre!
Ihm sei alles untertan!

2 Preis sei Gott für seine Gnade,
die er seinem Volk gewährt'.
Gottes Weg verläuft gerade,
auch wo Dunkel uns beschwert.
   Preis und Ehre, Preis und Ehre!
Gott im Himmel sei geehrt!

3 Wie ein Vater schenkt und lenkt er
unser Leben Tag für Tag,
trägt uns alle und bedenkt, wer
heute Hilfe brauchen mag.
   Preis und Ehre, Preis und Ehre!
Staub sind wir, doch er ist stark!

4 Preist den Herrn, ihr Engelscharen,
die ihr seinen Willen tut,
Sonne, Mond, ihr wunderbaren
Sterne auch mit eurer Glut.
   Preis und Ehre, Preis und Ehre!
Preis sei Gott, denn Gott ist gut!

209 PURIFY MY HEART
Refiner's fire

Words and music: Brian Doerksen
Spanish and German:
authorized translations

Prayerfully

1 Pur - i - fy__ my heart,__ let me be as gold and__ pre-cious sil - ver; pur - i - fy__ my heart,__ let me be as gold, pure__ gold.

2 Pur - i - fy__ my heart,__ cleanse me from with - in and__ make me ho - ly; pur - i - fy__ my heart,__ cleanse me from my sin, deep with - in.

Chorus

Re - fin - er's fire, my heart's one de - sire__

ESPAÑOL

1 *Purifícame,*
   hazme como oro y hermosa plata.
   Purifícame
   como el oro puro.
      Fuego de Dios, mi único anhelo
      es ser santo,
      ser apartado a ti, Dios.
      Elijo ser santo,
      se apartado a ti, mi Maestro
      y hacer tu voluntad.

2 *Purifícame*
   como el oro y hazme santo.
   Purifícame
   de mi pecado interior.
      Fuego de Dios . . .

DEUTSCH

1 *Reinige mein Herz,*
   laß mich sein wie Gold und feines Silber.
   Reinige mein Herz,
   laß mich sein wie Gold, reines Gold.
      Mit heil'ger Glut schmelz' aus, was Unrecht tut!
      Mach mich ganz heilig,
      ausgewählt dir zum Dienst, Herr!
      So will ich sein: heilig,
      fähig zu deinem Dienst, mein Meister,
      rein gemacht, heil und gut.

2 *Reinige mein Herz,*
   räume alles aus und mach mich heilig!
   Reinige mein Herz,
   tilg durch deine Huld alle Schuld.
      Mit heil'ger Glut schmelz' aus . . .

210 Rejoice, rejoice, Christ is in you
(Spanish and German versions)

Español
> ¡Gozaos! ¡gozaos! Cristo habita
> aquí, en vuestro corazón.
> ¡Él vive! ¡Él vive! en vosotros,
> sois un pueblo fuerto. ¡En pie!

1 Marchemos a la tierra que él nos prometó,
   él nos dará la victoria al luchar.
   Él marcha en majestad, nos guía en victoria.
   Verán que Cristo es el Señor.
   > ¡Gozaos! ¡gozaos . . .

2 Dios su propósito de cierto cumplirá,
   entre nosotros su Reino extenderá.
   Por fe lo imposible en él se hace realidad,
   démosle gloria sólo a él.
   > ¡Gozaos! ¡gozaos . . .

3 En mí debilidad su gracia suplirá.
   De barro soy más su fuerza está en mí.
   Un instrumento en tus manos yo quisiera ser.
   Toda la gloria es para ti.
   > ¡Gozaos! ¡gozaos . . .

Deutsch
> Seid froh! Seid froh! Christus in euch,
> die Hoffnung auf die Herrlichkeit.
> Er lebt! Er lebt! Sein Geist ist in euch,
> Steh auf in Kraft, Volk Gottes wir steh'n auf!

1 Die Zeit ist da, daß wir durchziehen unser Land,
   durch uns're Hand nimmt der Herr sein Erbe ein.
   Er kommt in Herrlichkeit, verleiht uns seinen Sieg im Streit,
   Die Welt soll seh'n, daß Jesus herrscht!
   > Seid froh! Seid froh . . .

2 Gott formt uns in sein Bild, sein Werk hier auszuführ'n,
   sein Reich zu baun in Kraft, nicht nur durchs Wort.
   Wo das Unmögliche durch Glauben an ihn möglich wird.
   Ehr' sei dem Herrn in Ewigkeit.
   > Seid froh! Seid froh . . .

3 Sind wir auch schwach, so reicht doch seine Gnade aus;
   wir sind nur Ton, doch mit Herrlichkeit erfüllt.
   Er zeugt in uns're Schwäche seine Macht und Herrlichkeit,
   Damit die Ehre ihm gehört.
   > Seid froh! Seid froh . . .

Music follows overleaf

210 REJOICE, REJOICE! CHRIST IS IN YOU

Words and music: Graham Kendrick
Spanish and German: authorized translations

Triumphantly

Chorus

Re - joice, re - joice! Christ is in you —the hope of glo - ry in our hearts. He lives, he lives! his breath is in you. A - rise! A might - y ar - my we a - rise!

Fine

Spanish and German versions on previous page

Verse

1 Now is the time for us __ to march up - on the land __ in - to our
2 God is at work in us __ his pur-pose to per-form __ build-ing a
3 Though we are weak, his grace is ev - ery-thing we need __ we're made of

hands he will give the ground we claim; __
king - dom of pow-er not __ of words; __
clay, but this trea-sure is __ with - in; __

he rides in ma - jes - ty __ to lead us in - to vic-to-ry, __
where things im - pos - si - ble __ by faith shall be made pos - si - ble: __
he turns our weak-ness-es __ in - to his op - por - tu - ni-ties,

the world shall see that Christ is Lord. __ Re -
let's give the glo - ry to him now. __ Re -
so that the glo - ry goes to him. __ Re -

211 SUCH LOVE

Flowing ♩ = 104

Words and music: Graham Kendrick
Spanish and German: authorized translations

Capo 4(C)

1 Such love, pure as the whit-est snow,
2 Such love, still-ing my rest-less-ness,
3 Such love springs from e-ter-ni-ty,

such love weeps for the shame I know,
such love, fill-ing my emp-ti-ness,
such love, stream-ing through his-to-ry,

such love, pay-ing the debt I owe
such love, show-ing me ho-li-ness
such love, foun-tain of life to me

O Je-sus, such love!
O Je-sus, such love!
O Je-sus, such love!

1 Qué amor, puro y santo;
   qué amor, mi vergüenza borró;
   qué amor, pagó mi deuda;
      ¡Oh Cristo, qué amor!

2 Qué amor, calmó mi inquietud;
   qué amor, mi vacío llenó;
   qué amor, me mostró santidad;
      ¡Oh Cristo, qué amor!

3 Qué amor, desde la eternidad;
   qué amor, por generaciones;
   qué amor, fuente de vida;
      ¡Oh Cristo, qué amor!

DEUTSCH

1 Welch Liebe, rein wie der weiße Schnee,
   welch Liebe in Schmach trug mein Weh,
   welch Liebe, die meine Schuld bezahlt,
      O Jesus, welch Liebe!

2 Welch Liebe, die meine Zweifel stillt,
   welch Liebe, die meine Leere füllt,
   welch Liebe, zeigt mir die Heiligkeit,
      O Jesus, welch Liebe!

3 Welch Liebe, strömt von der Ewigkeit,
   welch Liebe, fließt durch den Lauf der Zeit,
   welch Liebe, für mich der Lebensquell,
      O Jesus, welch Liebe!

212 THERE IS A REDEEMER

Words and music: Melody Green
Spanish and German: authorized translations
arranged David Peacock

1 There is a Redeemer,
2 Jesus, my Redeemer,
3 When I stand in glory

Jesus, God's own son, precious Lamb of
name above all names, precious Son of
I will see his face, and there I'll serve my

God, Messiah, holy One.
God, Messiah, Lamb for sinners slain:
king for ever in that holy place.

Words and music: © 1982 Birdwing Music / Cherry Lane Music, administered by CopyCare Ltd.,
PO Box 77, Hailsham, East Sussex BN27 3EF, UK. Used by permission.

ESPAÑOL

1 *Hay un Redentor,*
   el Hijo de Dios,
   cordero de Dios, Mesías,
   el Santísimo.
       Gracias Padre mío
       por entregar tu Hijo,
       y para terminar tu obra,
       has dado al Espíritu.

2 *Jesús, mi Redentor,*
   nombre sublime,
   cordero de Dios, Mesías,
   por nosotros murió.
       Gracias Padre mío . . .

3 *Cuando esté en gloria,*
   su Rostro veré.
   Siempre serviré a mi Rey,
   en el Santo Lugar.
       Gracias Padre mío . . .

DEUTSCH

1 *Er ist der Erlöser,*
   Jesus, Gottes Sohn;
   Gottes Lamm, erwählt zu tragen
   unserer Sünde Lohn.
       Danke lieber Vater,
       du gabst uns deinen Sohn.
       Dein Geist gibt uns die Kraft zu dienen
       bis er wiederkommt.

2 *Jesus, mein Erlöser,*
   höchster aller Namen,
   Gottes Lamm, erwählt zu tragen
   meiner Sünde Lohn.
       Danke lieber Vater . . .

3 *Einst werd' ich ihn sehen*
   in der Herrlichkeit.
   Meinem König werd' ich dienen
   bis in alle Ewigkeit.
       Danke lieber Vater . . .

213 To God be the glory
(Spanish and German versions)

ESPAÑOL

1 *A Dios demos gloria, pues grande es él;*
su amor es inmenso y a su Hijo nos dio:
quien fue a la cruz do sufrió muerte cruel,
y así de los cielos las puertas abrió.
    Dad loor al Señor,
    oiga el mundo su voz;
    dad loor al Señor,
    nos gozamos en Dios.
    Vengamos al Padre y a su Hijo Jesús,
    y démosle gloria por su gran poder.

2 *Por darnos la vida su sangro vertió;*
Jesús al creyente es promesa de Dios;
el vil pecador que de veras creyó
en ese momento perdón recibió.
    Dad loor al Señor . . .

3 *Dios es el Maestro, potente Hacedor,*
y grande es el gozo que Cristo nos da;
mas nuestro asombro será aún mayor
al ver a Jesús que en su gloria vendrá.
    Dad loor al Señor . . .

DEUTSCH

1 *O Gott, dir sei Ehre, der Großes getan!*
Du liebtest die Welt, nahmst der Sünder dich an!
Dein Sohn hat sein Leben zum Opfer geweiht.
Der Himmel steht offen zur ewigen Freud!
    Preist den Herrn! Preist den Herrn!
    Erde, hör' diesen Schall!
    Preist den Herrn! Preist den Herrn!
    Völker, freuet euch all!
    O kommt zu dem Vater! In Jesus wir nah'n.
    Und gebt ihm die Ehre, der Großes getan.

2 *O große Erlösung, erkauft durch sein Blut!*
Dem Sünder, der glaubt, kommt sie heute zugut!
Die volle Vergebung wird jedem zuteil,
der Jesus erfasset, das göttliche Heil.
    Preist den Herrn . . .

3 *Wie groß ist sein Lieben! Wie groß ist sein Tun!*
Wie groß unser Freude, in Jesus zu ruhn!
Doch größer und reiner und höher wirds sein,
wenn jubelnd und schauend wir droben ziehn ein.
    Preist den Herrn . . .

Music follows overleaf

213 TO GOD BE THE GLORY

Words: F. J. van Alstyne
Spanish: Roberto C. Savage
German: Lotte Sauer
Music: W. H. Doane

1 To God be the glory! Great things he has done;
2 O per-fect re-demp-tion, the pur-chase of blood!
3 Great things he has taught us, great things he has done,

so loved he the world that he gave us his Son
to ev-ery be-liev-er the pro-mise of God:
and great our re-joic-ing through Je-sus the Son:

who yield-ed his life an a-tone-ment for sin,
the vil-est of-fend-er who tru-ly be-lieves,
but pur-er and high-er and great-er will be

Spanish and German versions on previous page

and   o‐pened the   life‐gate that   all   may   go   in.
that   mo‐ment from   Je‐sus   a   par‐don   re‐ceives.
our   won‐der,   our   glad‐ness, when   Je‐sus   we   see!

Chorus

Praise the Lord,   praise the Lord!   let the earth hear his   voice;

praise the Lord,   praise the Lord!   let the   peo‐ple   re‐joice:

O   come__   to the   Fa‐ther through   Je‐sus   the   Son

and   give him   the   glo‐ry – great   things he   has   done.

214 WHAT A FRIEND WE HAVE IN JESUS

CONVERSE

Words: J.M. Scriven
Spanish: Leandro Gaza Mora
German: Ernst Gebhardt
Music: C. C. Converse

1 What a friend we have in Je - sus, all our sins and griefs to bear;
2 Have we tri - als and temp - ta - tions, is there trou - ble a - ny - where?
3 Are we weak and hea - vy - la - den bur - dened with a load of care?

what a pri - vi - lege to car - ry ev - ery - thing to God in prayer!
We should ne - ver be dis - cour - aged: take it to the Lord in prayer.
Je - sus is our migh - ty sav - iour: he will lis - ten to our prayer.

O what peace we oft - en for - feit, O what need - less pain we bear,
Can we find a friend so faith - ful who will all our sor - rows share?
Do your friends des - pise, for - sake you? take it to the Lord in prayer;

all be - cause we do not car - ry ev - ery - thing to God in prayer.
Je - sus knows our ev - ery weak - ness — take it to the Lord in prayer.
in his arms he will en - fold you and his love will shield you there.

1 *¡Oh qué amigo nos es Cristo!*
El llevó nuestro dolor,
y nos manda que llevemos
todo a Dios en oración.
¿Vive el hombre desprovisto
de paz, gozo y santo amor?
Esto es porque no llevamos
todo a Dios en oración.

2 *Jesucristo es nuestro amigo,*
de esto prueba nos mostró,
pues sufrió el cruel castigo
que el culpable mereció.
El castigo de su pueblo
en su muerte él sufrió;
Cristo un amigo eterno;
¡Sólo en él confío yo!

3 *¿Vives débil y cargado*
de cuidados y temor?
A Jesús, refugio eterno,
dile todo en oración.
¿Te desprecian tus amigos?
Cuéntaselo en oración;
en sus brazos de amor tierno
paz tendrá tu corazón.

1 *Welch ein Freund ist unser Jesus,*
o wie hoch ist er erhöht!
Er hat uns mit Gott versöhnet
und vertritt uns im Gebet.
Wer mag sagen und ermessen,
wieviel Segen uns entgeht,
wenn wir nicht zu ihm uns wenden
und ihn suchen im Gebet.

2 *Wenn des Feindes Macht und drohet*
und manch Sturm rings um uns weht,
brauchen wir uns nicht zu fürchten,
stehn wir gläubig im Gebet.
Da erweist sich Jesu Treue,
wie er uns zur Seite steht
als ein mächtiger Erretter,
der erhört ein ernst Gebet.

3 *Sind mit Sorgen wir beladen,*
sei es frühe oder spät,
hilft uns sicher unser Jesus,
fliehn zu ihm wir im Gebet.
Sind von Freunden wir verlassen
und wir gehen ins Gebet,
o so ist uns Jesus alles:
König, Priester und Prophet.

215 WHEN I SURVEY

ROCKINGHAM

Words: Isaac Watts
Spanish: W. T. Millham
German: Günter Balders
Music: adapted E. Miller

1 When I___ sur - vey the won - drous cross
2 For - bid___ it, Lord, that I___ should boast
3 See from___ his head, his hands,___ his___ feet,
4 Were the___ whole realm of na - ture___ mine,

on which the prince of glo - ry died,___
save in the cross of Christ___ my God:___
sor - row and love flow ming - led down:___
that were an of - fering far___ too small;___

my rich - est gain I count___ as loss,
the ve - ry things that charm___ me most –
when did such love and sor - row meet
love so a - maz - ing, so di - vine,

| E♭ | B♭ | E♭ | Fm | E♭ | E♭/B♭ | B♭7 | E♭ |
| (D) | (A) | (D) | (Em) | (D) | | (A7) | (D) |

and pour___ con - tempt on all___ my___ pride.
I sac - ri - fice them to___ his___ blood.
or thorns___ com - pose so rich___ a___ crown?
de - mands___ my soul, my life,___ my___ all!

ESPAÑOL

1 La cruz excelsa al contemplar
do Cristo allí por mí murió,
nada se puede comparar
a las riquezas de su amor.

2 Yo no me quiero, Dios, gloriar
mas que en la muerte del Señor.
Lo que más pueda ambicionar
lo doy gozoso por su amor.

3 Ved en su rostro, manos, pies,
las marcas vivas del dolor;
es imposible comprender
tal sufrimiento y tanto amor.

4 El mundo entero no será
dádiva digna de ofrecer.
Amor tan grande, sin igual
en cambio exige rodo el ser.

DEUTSCH

1 Schau ich zu deinem Kreuze hin,
wo du für mich gestorben bist,
zu Schaden wird, was sonst Gewinn,
was einst mein Stolz gewesen ist.

2 Dein Kreuz zerstört den falschen Ruhm;
durch deinen Tod bin ich befreit,
gebunden als dein Eigentum
an dich allein für allezeit.

3 Sieh an sein dorngekröntes Haupt,
aus seinen Wunden quillt sein Blut;
und wer an solche Liebe glaubt,
dem kommt sein Kreuzesschmerz zugut.

4 Was ich zum Dank auch gebe dir,
die ganze Welt ist noch zu klein;
der Dank für diese Liebe hier
kann nur mein eignes Leben sein.

216 WHEN I LOOK INTO YOUR HOLINESS

Words and music: Wayne and Cathy Perrin
Spanish and German: authorized translations
arranged G. Baker

When I look in-to your ho - li - ness,_ when I gaze in-to your love - li -

- ness, when all things that sur-round be-come sha-dows in the light of

you;_____ when I've found the joy of reach-ing your

heart,_ when my will be-comes en-thralled with your love, when all

ESPAÑOL

Cuando miro yo tu santidad
Y me gozo en tu gran amor.
Todas mis sombras se desvanecen
en tu hermosa luz.
Descubriendo toda la alegria
de vivir haciendo tu voluntad,
todas mis sombras se desvanecen
en tu hermosa luz.
    Yo te adoro, yo te adoro,
    Yo vivo Señor,
    para honrarte a ti.
    Yo te adoro, yo te adoro,
    yo vivo Señor,
    para honrarte a ti.

DEUTSCH

Wenn ich deine Heiligkeit bestaune,
deine Schönheit klar vor Augen sen',
dann wäre alles um mich wie ein Schatten
    in deinem Licht.
Wenn ich deine Nahe deutlich spüre
deine Liebe vollig mich umhüllt,
dann wird alles um mich wie ein Schatten
    in deinem Licht.
    Ich bete dich an, ich bete dich an –
    dich allein anzubeten ist meines Lebens Sinn,
    ich bete dich an, ich bete dich an –
    dich allein auzubeten ist meines Lebens Sinn.

217 Yours be the glory
(Spanish and German versions)

ESPAÑOL

1 Tuya es la gloria, victorioso Redentor,
porque tú la muerte venciste, Señor.
Quitan la gran piedra ángeles de luz,
y en la tumba el lienzo guardan, oh Jesús.
Tuya es la gloria,
victorioso Redentor,
porque tú la muerte
venciste, Señor.

2 Vemos que llega el resucitado ya;
ansias y temores él nos quitará.
Que su iglesia alegre cante la canción:
¡Vivo está! ¡La muerte pierde su aguijón!
Tuya es la gloria . . .

3 ¡Ya no dudamos, Príncipe de vida y paz!
Sin ti no valemos; fortaleza das,
más que vencedores haznos por tu amor,
y al hogar celeste llévanos, Señor.
Tuya es la gloria . . .

DEUTSCH

1 Dein ist Macht und Ehre, ewig dein der Sieg.
Held der aus dem Grabe sieggekrönt entstieg.
Wir auch sollen leben mit dem Herrn zugleich,
Er will uns erheben in sein himmlisch Reich.
Dein ist Macht und Ehre,
ewig dein der Sieg.
Held, der aus dem Grabe
sieggekrönt entstieg.

2 Auf unser Flehen gibt er und vergibt.
Jeder kann es sehen, daß er lebt und liebt.
Volk des Herrn, o freue deines Königs dich!
Seine Huld und Treue währet ewiglich.
Dein ist Macht und Ehre . . .

3 Was kann uns scheiden von der Liebe sein?
Trübsal oder Leiden, irgendeine Pein!
Wovor soll mir grauen? Als ein Kind des Lichts
darf ich ihm vertrauen: Nein, ich fürchte nichts.
Dein ist Macht und Ehre . . .

Music follows overleaf

217 YOURS BE THE GLORY

Words: after E. Budry, R. B. Hoyle
in this version Jubilate Hymns
Music: G. F. Handel

Capo 3(C)

1 Yours be the glo - ry! ri - sen,__ con-quering Son;
2 See! Je - sus meets us, ri - sen__ from the tomb,
3 No more we doubt you, glo - rious prince of life:

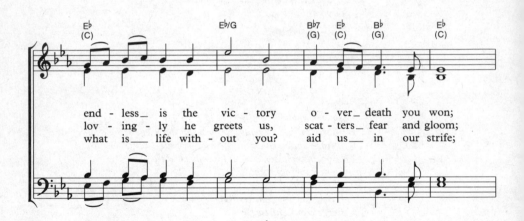

end - less__ is the vic - tory o - ver__ death you won;
lov - ing - ly he greets us, scat - ters__ fear and gloom;
what is__ life with - out you? aid us__ in our strife;

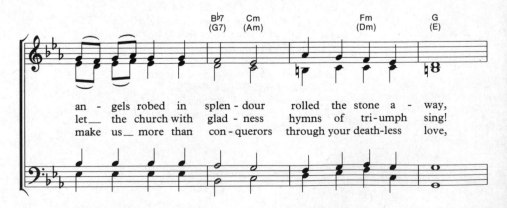

an - gels robed in splen - dour rolled the stone a - way,
let__ the church with glad - ness hymns of tri - umph sing!
make us__ more than con - querors through your death-less love,

Spanish and German versions on previous page

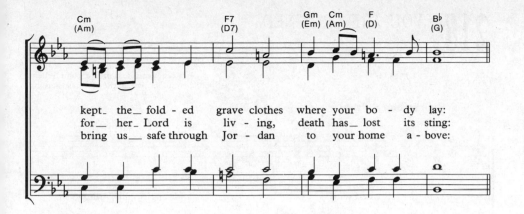

kept_ the_ fold - ed grave clothes where your bo - dy lay:
for_ her_ Lord is liv - ing, death has_ lost its sting:
bring us_ safe through Jor - dan to your home a - bove:

Yours be the glo - ry! ri - sen,_ con-quering Son;

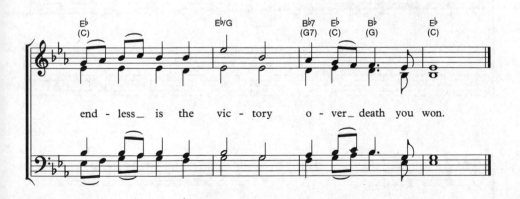

end - less_ is the vic - tory o - ver_ death you won.

218 YOU ARE CROWNED

Words and music: John Sellers
Spanish and German: authorized translations

With a strong rhythm

You are crowned with ma-ny crowns and rule all things in right-eous-ness; you are crowned with ma-ny crowns, up-hold-ing all things by your word. You rule_ in pow-er_ and reign_ in glo - ry,

you are___ the Lord of hea - ven and___

earth, you are Lord of

all,_____ you are Lord of

1.
all!_____

2.
all!_____

ESPAÑOL

Coronado tú estás
y riges todo con justicia.
Coronado tú estás
sostienes todo con tu palabra.
Riges con poder y en gloria reinas;
tú eres Señor de cielo y tierra.
Tú eres Señor,
tú eres Señor.

DEUTSCH

Reich gekrönt bist du, oh Herr,
als Herrscher in Gerechtigkeit.
Reich gekrönt bist du, oh Herr,
du trägst die Welten durch dein Wort.
Du herrscht in Kraft, du regierst in Herrlichkeit,
du bist der Herr von Himmel und Erd'!
Du allein bist Herr,
du allein bist Herr!

COPYRIGHT ADDRESSES

A & C Black (Publishers) Ltd, Howard Road, Eaton Socon, Huntingdon, Cambs PE19 3EZ

Asian School of Music, Worship and the Arts, P. O. Box 10533, Quezon City 1112, The Philippines

Asociacion Bautista Argentina de Publicationes (A. B. A. P.), Av, Ricadavia 3464, 1203 Buenos Aires, Argentina

Asociacion Ediciones La Aurora, 1244 Buenos Aires, Argentina

Atkins, Robert, c/o M Phillips, 24 Ty-Bryn Hill, Abertillery, Gwent

Blenkinsop, Alison, 11a Grayham Road, New Malden, Surrey KT3 5HR

CanZion Producciones, Apdo. post C-62, Dutango, Dgo 34241, Mexico

Caribbean Conference of Churches, P. O. Box 616, Bridgetown, Barbados, West Indies

Cartford, Gerhard, 2279 Commonwealth Avenue, St. Paul, Michigan 55108, USA

China Christian Council, 17 Da Jian Yin Xian, Nanjing, China

Choristers' Guild, The, 2834 W. Kingsley Road, Garland, Texas 75041-2498, USA

Christ Church Gospel Band, Diocese of Enugu, Christ Church Parish, Uwani, PMB 424, Enugu, Nigeria

Christian Conference of Asia, Pak Tin Village, Mei Tin Road, Shatin, N. T., Hong Kong

CopyCare Ltd, P. O. Box 77, Hailsham, East Sussex BN27 3EF

CopyCare Deutschland, Postfach 1220, D-73762 Neuhausen, Stuttgart, Germany

Dargie, Dave, Melusinenstrasse 13, 8000 München 80, Germany

Duba, Arlo D., 111 Lake South Terrace, Hot Springs, Arkansas 7193, USA

Evangelical Church of Finland, P. O. B. 185, SE-00161, Helsinki, Finland

Faber Music Ltd, 3 Queen Square, London WC1N 2AU

Friedrich Villia Verlag, Hamburg, Germany

Hänssler Verlag, Postfach 1220, D/W-73762 Neuhausen, Stuttgart, Germany

Harling, Per, Ton-Vis Produktion AB, Box 92, 193 22 Sigtuna, Sweden

Hope Publishing Company, 380 South Main Place, Carol Stream, Illinois 60188, USA

Jubilate Hymns, c/o Mrs B Grundy, 61 Chessel Avenue, Southampton SO19 4DY (copyrights owned by Jubilate Hymns are administered in the USA and Canada by Hope Publishing Company)

Kingsway's Thankyou Music, P. O. Box 75, Eastbourne, East Sussex BN23 6NW

Kroma Producciones Evangelicas, Cami de Sta. Lucia, 12/2m 03700 Denia, Alicante, Spain

Lee, Geonyong, Korean National Institute of Arts, 700 Seocho-Dong, Seocho-ku, Seoul, Korea

Lutheran World Foundation, P. O. Box 2100, 150 Route de Ferney, CH-1211, Geneva 20, Switzerland

Make Way Music Ltd, P. O. Box 263, Croydon, Surrey CR9 5AP

Maldonado, Dr Jorge, Centro Hispano de Estudios Teologics, 6133 Clara Street, Bell Gardens, California 90201, USA

Maraschin, Jaci C., Rue Rego Freitas 530, E-13, 01220-010 Sao Paulo, SP Brazil

Mxadana, G, c/o ISM (Pty) Ltd, P O Box 1419, Johannesburg 2000, Republic of South Africa

Oncken Verlag, Wuppertal, Postfach 2220, D-42766 Haan, Germany

Parkman, Lars, Utryck, Box 3039, S-75003 Uppsala, Sweden

Perkio, Pia, Stenbackinkatu 5 A 7, SP-00250 Helsinki, Finland

Popkes, Wiard, Reunbahustrasse 445, D-22111 Hamburg, Germany

Reindorf, Dinah, P. O. Box 19060, Accra, Ghana

Reith, Angela, 47 Mayton Street, London N7 6QP

Reveil, B. P. 719, 26007 Valence Cedex, France

Sandwell, Peter, PS! Production, Dalskog, 570 22 Forserum, Sweden

Solis, Melchizedek and Mutya, 104 E. Lamar Street, Salinary, California 93906, USA

Stainer & Bell Ltd, P. O. Box 110 Victoria House, Gruneisen Road, Finchley, London N3 1DZ

Taizé, Ateliers et Presses de, Taizé Community, F71250, France

Turmezei, Erzebet, Karacsony Sandor utca 31-22, H-1086 Budapest, Hungary

Ungdom i Oppdrag, 2312 Ottestad, Norway

United Methodist Church Service, Mutambara, CPS Box 61, Cashel, Zimbabwe

World Council of Churches Publications, 150 Route de Ferney, P. O. Box 2100, 1211 Geneva 2, Switzerland

WGRG, Iona Community, Community House, Pearce Institute, Govan, Glasgow G51 3UU, Scotland

Yanapa, Zeilo, Cepita, Casilla 10221, La Paz, Bolivia

Zabolotski, Orof Nikolai, 27b Chemin Terrinx, 1218 Geneva, Switzerland

THEMATIC INDEX

COUNTRY INDEX

El Salvador

Danos un corazón grande para
    amar-26
Santo, santo, santo-128
Te alabarán, oh Señor-140

Guatemala

Entonemos un canto de
    alabanza-34

Mexico

Alza tus ojos-6
En ti confia mi corazón-33
Heme aquí-59
Te exaltamos-144

Nicaragua

Sent by the Lord am I-131

Peru

Glory to God-42

MAIN INDEX

Hymns and Songs of the Worldwide Church:

(Italics denote alternative titles)

A baby was born in Bethlehem-1

Ahsante Yesu-2

Alabad a Jehová-3

All is made for the glory of God (Tout est fait pour la gloire de Dieu)-153

All the kings of the earth (Te alabarán, oh Señor)-140

All who are thirsty-4

Alleluia-5

Alleluia (Zamiranza)-171

Alleluia! We sing your praises (Haleluya! Pelo tsa rona)-49

Alza tus ojos-6

Amahoro benedata-7

Amen, alleluia!-8

Amen, siakudumisa!-9

Amen, we praise your name, O God (Amen, siakudumisa!)-9

Ante tu presencia-10

Ay Ay Salidumay (Glory to the Lord of love)-45

Bani ngyeti Ba Yawe-11

Bia nene ifeoma-12

Bolo jay, mikar jay-13

Brothers and sisters (Ty wyzwoliles nas)-157

By the Babylonian rivers-14

By the waters of Babylon-15

Cantai ao Senhor-16

Cast your burdens (Hiya, hiya)-17

Christ is all to me-18

Christ is risen (Cristo vive)-25

Christ's is the world in which we move-19

Chu yǒ sa sǔ mi shi naen mul-22

Clear and calm the night-20

Come now with joyful and thankful hearts-21

Come now, O Prince of peace-23

Come to be our hope, Lord Jesus (Vem, Jesus nossa esperança)-159

Come walk with us (Hamba nathi)-52

Come, O Holy Spirit, come (Wa wa wa Emimimo)-160

Come, let us celebrate the day (Nagarikudzwe zuva)-111

Cordero ng Diyos-24

Cristo vive-25

Danos un corazón grande para amar-26

Där Guds Ande är-27

Dios es nuestro amparo-28

Du är helig-29

El Señor és la meva força-32

El cielo canta alegría-31

En ti confia mi corazón-33

Entonemos un canto de alabanza-34

Everything is yours, Lord (Tata pokelela)-138

Ewuradze-30

Far beyond our mind's grasp (Hindi ko maisip)-60

Father in heaven-38

Father in heaven (Ishworo)-72

Food to pilgrims-35

For the beauty of the earth-36

Free to serve-37

Gabi, Gabi-40

Get together-39

Ginoo malooy ka kanamo-41

Give praise to the Lord (Purihin ang Panginoon)-123

Gloria, gloria-44

Gloria, gloria, gloria-43

Glory, glory, glory (Gloria, gloria, gloria)-43

Glory to God-42

Glory to God (Gloria, gloria)-44

Glory to God (Maw hee ma)-100

Glory to the Lord of love-45

Glory, glory, hallelujah (Tukutendereza Yesu)-154

Go in Jesus' name (Id y predicad)-67

God sent his son-46

God's fire (Moto umewaka leo)-102

God, be praised at early morn (Qingchen zao)-124

God, give us a new heart (Danos un corazón grande para amar)-26

Great God of power and might (Onyame kokroko)-119

Ha- ha- ha- halelluiah-47

Haleluya! Pelo tsa rona-49

Halle, halle, hallelujah-48

Halleluja, halleluja du er Gud-50

Hallelujah-51

Hallelujah, hallelujah, you are God (Halleluja, halleluja du er Gud)-50

Hamba nathi-52

Hanúre binnanún-53

Have mercy on us, Lord (Khudaya, rahem kar)-82

Have you ever seen-54

Hay momentos-55

He came down-56

He has arisen, alleluia! (Mfurahini, halleluya)-104

He is risen-58

He was born a little child-57

Heaven is singing for joy (El cielo canta alegría)-31

Heme aquí-59

Here I am (Heme aquí)-59

Here I am, the one (Kata ku na ni mo shu o koba mi nu)-79

Here within your presence (Ante tu presencia)-10

International hymns and songs: